# Putting Away Childish Things

## WORKBOOK

# Putting Away Childish Things
## WORKBOOK

A Recovery Workbook for
*Putting Away Childish Things*

David A. Seamands
and Beth Funk

VICTOR BOOKS
A DIVISION OF SCRIPTURE PRESS PUBLICATIONS INC.
USA CANADA ENGLAND

**Other Victor Books Titles by David Seamands**

*Freedom from the Performance Trap*

*Healing of Memories*

*Living with Your Dreams*

*Healing for Damaged Emotions*

Unless otherwise noted, Scripture quotations are from the *New American Standard Bible* , © the Lockman Foundation 1960, 1962, 1963, 1968, 1971, 1972, 1973, 1975, 1977. Other quotations are from the *King James Version* (KJV); *The New Testament in Modern English*, Revised Edition (PH), © J.B. Phillips, 1958, 1960, 1972, permission of Macmillan Publishing Co. and Collins Publishers; the *Holy Bible, New International Version* ® (NIV). Copyright © 1973, 1978, 1984 by International Bible Society. Used by permission of Zondervan Publishing House. All rights reserved. *The Revised Standard Version of the Bible* (RSV), © 1946, 1952, 1971, 1973; *The New Revised Standard Version of the Bible* (NRSV), © 1989; *The Modern Language Bible: The Berkeley Version in Modern English* (MLB), © 1945, 1959, 1969 by Zondervan Publishing House; the *New English Bible* (NEB), © The Delegates of the Oxford University Press and the Syndics of the Cambridge University Press, 1961, 1970. Used by permission. And *The Holy Bible: New Century Version* (NCV), © Word Publishing 1987, 1988, 1991. Used by permission. All rights reserved.

Recommended Dewey Decimal Classification: 200.19 or 152.92
Suggested Subject Headings: CHRISTIAN LIVING; RECOVERY

ISBN: 1-56476-194-0

© 1993 by SP Publications, Inc. All rights reserved. Printed in the United States of America

1 2 3 4 5 6 7 8 9 10 Printing/Year 97 96 95 94 93

*To Helen*
*who for forty years*
*by her unconditional love,*
*understanding humor,*
*and unyielding confrontation*
*has helped me put away*
*many of my childish things.*

# CONTENTS

# PREFACE

I used to think that as a person entered adulthood his childish behavior patterns gradually fell away and new adult patterns took their place. But I have discovered that this is not true. Many people who are chronological adults are still emotional and spiritual children. Their quantity of birthdays may reveal their age in life, but their quality of behavior reveals their stage in life—childhood.

The New Testament tells us we are to *katargeo* childish behavior patterns and attitudes that are keeping us from maturity. This Greek word means "to put away, to render inoperative, inactive, or powerless; to remove the meaning and significance from; to cause a person to be free from something that has been binding him."

The Apostle Paul described his own growth transition this way: "When I was a little child I talked and felt and thought like a little child. Now that I am a man, my childish speech and feeling and thought have no further significance for me" (1 Corinthians 13:11, PH). "I've given up the ways of a child" (MLB).

*Katargeo* is a strong verb. And putting it into practice requires great effort and struggle if we are to emerge from the fight victorious and grown-up. Childish things don't simply fall away by themselves as dead leaves fall from a tree. We have to put them away, *katargeo* them, and be "finished with childish things" (NEB).

These chapters have been written to help identify some of our outdated childish patterns, and to suggest ways of breaking their grip upon us, so we can "grow up in every way into Christ" (Ephesians 4:15, PH).

*David A. Seamands*
*Wilmore, Kentucky*
*1982*

# INTRODUCTION

Sadly enough, many of us were raised in households where there was deprivation and abuse. The result is that we have "grown up" chronologically, but not emotionally or spiritually. Childish thinking and ways of behaving keep us from "growing up" and becoming all that God has in mind for us to be. That is what this workbook is all about. It is designed to give you tools to move beyond "childish things" to the maturity God desires for you.

What makes this workbook different from the original work of the same title is that you now have an opportunity to *journal* your way through the entire text of *Putting Away Childish Things*. Questions have been inserted into the text at key places to help you personalize and record your thoughts, feelings, and experiences along the way.

Journal writing is a time-honored practice that dates back as far as the confessions of St. Augustine and the spiritual diaries of the Quakers. This discipline can serve you well in your individual program of personal growth and healing as you remain open to the Holy Spirit's work in your life. No matter how much hurt you have experienced in the past, you have the choice of opening yourself up to God's love and healing power through the Holy Spirit. As you write down your thoughts and feelings in response to the questions asked throughout the text, the Holy Spirit will gently bring the truth about your past to light and "the truth will set you free" (John 8:32).

## HOW EACH CHAPTER IS ORGANIZED

There are four basic elements included in every chapter of this workbook. They are:

■ **The entire text of *Putting Away Childish Things*.** This book was first published in 1982 and has helped thousands of readers deal honestly and sensitively with the wounds of their childhood. It is possible that you have at one point or another already read this book. But don't let that stop you from going through it again—*Putting Away Childish Things* is a book well worth rereading.

■ **Personal Reflection.** Key questions and reflection exercises have been built into the text to help you filter the truth of the text through the grid of your own experience. Here is where much healing can take place. Application of truth to life leads to transformation. The merits of journaling have already been cited in the paragraphs above. You will greatly benefit from this book by taking time to write down your answers in the space provided. If you are unable to answer a question as you work through the material the first time, move on. The goal is NOT to answer every question. The goal is to get in touch with as much truth as is possible for you. Remember: God does not violate us, invade us, force Himself upon us, or overtake us. As you remain open to Him, the Holy Spirit will gently affirm to you that God can be trusted. He does have your best interest at heart. So trust Him. He will guide you as you read and write your way through this workbook.

■ **Prayerful Reflection.** Prayer is both talking to and hearing from God. At the end of each chapter you will have an opportunity to tell God in writing how you feel about the things you have read. Exercise rigorous honesty with Him. Dare to entrust your deepest fears and secrets to Him. Then listen carefully to hear what He has to say. God will meet you at your place of need.

■ **Personal Renewal.** The final exercise in each chapter is a meditation or memorization activity. One way your life will be transformed is through the "renewing of your mind" (Romans 12:2). The Bible is the primary sourcebook God has given us for renewing our minds. Hear what the writer of Hebrews tells us about God's Word: "[It] is alive and working and is sharper than a double-edged sword. It cuts all the way into us, where the soul and the spirit are joined, to the center of our joints and bones. And it judges the thoughts and feelings in our hearts" (Hebrews 4:12, NCV). Each Scripture in this section reflects a key truth the author writes about in the chapter. Meditate and memorize (wherever possible) the passages listed. God can use His Word to bring tremendous healing to your thoughts and feelings.

## HOW TO USE THIS BOOK

*Putting Away Childish Things* is a workbook that presents a series of writing exercises and ideas for personal growth and development. This material is designed for use by individuals as well as groups. No matter what approach you take in using the material, there are some basic guidelines to follow.

### Individual Study
Pace yourself through each chapter, taking whatever time you need to complete the Personal Reflection, Prayerful Reflection, and Personal Renewal exercises as you read. You may get through all of the exercises in one sitting, or you may choose to spread your writing out over a longer period of time. Be patient with yourself. Give yourself time to digest the content of each chapter and reflect on its meaning. Share what you are learning with someone you trust.

Do not feel obligated to complete every exercise. However, if you find yourself avoiding a particular exercise or chapter, take a good look at your resistance and then make a special effort to work in that area of the book. This may be precisely the chapter or exercise that can really begin to help you heal.

Write out your answers fully. Don't use just a word or short phrase, but write complete sentences and paragraphs. You will find that the process of writing will help you gain awareness and perspectives that you may not have known you had.

As you work the material in this book you may be surprised at the power of the feelings that come up as you write. Give yourself permission to feel your feelings. Denying your feelings will only slow down the healing process; acknowledging them will speed it up and bring about the emotional and spiritual healing you desire.

### Group Study

We are broken in the context of relationship, and we are also healed within the scope of relationships. Though there is great value in working the exercises in this book individually, you will find that your healing process is enhanced and accelerated by the mutual support and encouragement that is found in a small group setting.

Appendix One of this workbook gives you complete guidelines for using this material in groups. There is a Personal Journey Summary Sheet provided for each chapter of the book, plus a "Telling My Story" page that should be used the first time the group meets together. The group material has been designed in such a way that it is virtually self-facilitating. If you can read, you can lead. The success of the group is not dependent on one individual. Rather, it is the combined efforts of and group members' mutual commitment to the group process that will bring about an emotionally and spiritually satisfying outcome. Group members will receive maximum benefit from the group process if they have taken time during the week to complete the writing exercises that are in Part 1 of the workbook.

Ideally, a group meeting should last one-and-a-half to two hours. Try to start and end each meeting on time. At your first meeting, communicate clearly the Guidelines for Group Sharing (also found in Appendix One). These guidelines will help provide a safe environment for group members. Safety is essential to the healing process. And confidentiality is essential to feeling safe. You will find additional facilitator helps in Appendix One at the back of this workbook to help you in your group process.

## THE VALUE OF SUPPORT

Christ-centered and secular self-help support groups have flourished in the past decade. These groups strive to create a safe and nurturing environment where members can face and learn to effectively deal with the pain in their lives. It helps to know that someone else cares and is willing to share his or her experience, strength, and hope with us along the way.

Solomon, in the Book of Ecclesiastes, had this to say about the value of supportive relationships: "Two are better than one, because they have a good return for their work: If one falls down, his friend can help him up. But pity the man who falls and has no one to help him up! . . . Though one may be overpowered, two can defend themselves. A cord of three strands is not quickly broken" (Ecclesiastes 4:9-10, 12, NIV). Make a wise choice—employ the power of group dynamics to help you find healing for damaged emotions. You are not alone.

# PART ONE

*For we know in part, and we prophesy in part; but when the perfect comes, the partial will be done away. When I was a child, I used to speak as a child, think as a child, reason as a child; when I became a man, I did away with childish things.*

*1 Corinthians 13:9-11*

# Chapter 1
# The Hidden Child in Us All

Somewhere, sometime, you were a child. Although you don't remember all the details of your childhood, the child and teenager you once were is still important to you today because it continues to exist within you. The hidden child of your past is very much alive and affects everything that you do, for good or for ill.

William Wadsworth was right—"The child is father of the man." You cannot cut yourself off from your own history. You are a complex tapestry, woven with a million strands, some of which reach back to Adam and beyond him to God who created you in His image. But many of the most important threads in the complex design of who you are were introduced in your childhood, especially in the parent-child relationships.

The hidden child within can be a determining factor in life. He can lead and he can also mislead. In some people, the inner child not only survives but thrives as a bawling, brawling, sprawling character. He noisily rushes into activities he likes. He interferes with present adult life. He hurts and destroys the most meaningful relationships.

Or perhaps that inner child of your past is so timid, fearful, defeated, and self-despising that no matter how much you want to, you just can't force yourself to make friends, or speak up when you have an opinion to express, or handle heavy responsibility. He may keep you from becoming the person you have the potential of being.

---

**PERSONAL
REFLECTION**

■ Find a photograph of yourself as a child. Spend time studying it before pasting it in the space provided on the next page.

**PLACE YOUR CHILDHOOD PHOTO HERE**

■ Write a description of yourself as a child. Try to recall in as much detail as you can the child you remember being. Focus more on who you were than on what you did. *NOTE: Additional journaling pages have been provided in the back of this workbook should you need more space for writing.*

_____

_____

_____

_____

_____

■ As an adult, have you ever behaved in a way that was viewed by others, or felt to you like it was childish and inappropriate? Describe how you behaved and explain why you think you behaved as you did. What response did the behavior elicit from other adults?

_____

_____

_____

Because of the power wielded by your inner child, it is essential you know this part of yourself. However, it is necessary to insert a word of caution. We live in a psyched-up world. Everyone who has had Psychology 101 is an amateur analyst. And the greatest wrong in misguided probing is that a lot of folks like to dig around in their past to find excuses for their present behavior. They want to be able to say, "My mother and dad, my brother, my circumstances, my teacher, or that accident made me what I am today. If only this . . . if only that . . . then I would be OK."

In contrast to this self-defeating irresponsibility, I ask that you look back to find out where you are still allowing the inner child of your past to dominate your life, in order that you may become more responsible. Look back to discover where you need to change, where you need to forgive and be forgiven, where you need to be healed, and where you need to daily discipline yourself. Look back so that you may be yourself as you really were intended to be a child of God set free by the healing power of the Holy Spirit.

As you discover where this inner hidden child is defeating you, you can *katargeo* him. You can break his power and render him inoperative. You can abrogate his sway so that you will be free to grow up in Christ in every way, especially into the perfect love which will make you a victorious and fruit-bearing disciple.

## PERSONAL REFLECTION

■ In what ways does the inner child of your past continue to dominate your life in the present? To help you complete this writing exercise, ask yourself these questions: In what ways do I still need to change? Is there anyone in my life, past or present, who I am holding a grudge against or with whom I've severed a relationship because of hurt feelings? Are there any areas of my life where I continue to exhibit a need for emotional healing (e.g., fear of new relationships; inability to complete projects; telling little "white lies")? Are there any areas of my life where I struggle to maintain personal discipline?

_____

_____

_____

_____

_____

■ How much power does your inner child wield in your life at present? Do you view the power your inner child has in your life as constructive or destructive power? Explain why.

_____

_____

_____

_____

_____

_____

About twenty years ago, Hugh Missildine, a psychologist, wrote a best-selling book called *Your Inner Child of the Past* (Simon and Schuster). It is still a classic in its field and has been of great value in showing how the various attitudes of our parents affect the way we develop our own personality traits. I am deeply indebted to Missildine for some of the concepts used in this chapter.

This little child of the past makes himself most clearly known in the place where a child is most comfortable—the home, and in those personal contact and relationships which feel most like home. The hardest place to live maturely is with close friends, a roommate, a sweetheart, colleagues at work, and with family. For the little child tends to take over in close relationships.

When we are living in a casual way, we put on public selves that are polite and well-controlled. In our shallow contacts with people we usually are very grown-up, reasonable, and nice to be with. But let us move into a close personal relationship such as a deep friendship, love, marriage, or a close working partnership, and how quickly that little inner child of the past can take over. He may become unreasonable, stubborn, and demanding, or shy, fearful, and weak. We can become such completely different persons that we are surprised and shocked by what we think and feel and say.

## PERSONAL REFLECTION

■ In what ways do you identify with what the author describes in the previous two paragraphs? Create a word picture of your public self. Then describe your private self. How closely do the two pictures of your two selves line up?

My Public Self _____

_____

_____

_____

My Private Self _____

_____

_____

_____

■ It's true that the hardest place to live maturely is with the people who are closest to us. Can you think of any recent instances when you responded in an immature way to something that was happening? Describe what happened and how you responded to what happened.

_____

_____

_____

_____

_____

_____

_____

■ How honest are you able to be with yourself when someone you love confronts you about an immature behavior? Reality test your answer to this question with someone who knows you well.

_____

_____

_____

_____

If we stop to honestly look at our behavior, we may discover that we really haven't reacted to the present situation as it is. Rather, that hidden child of the past has surfaced to respond to some childhood event or relationship. We have not acted with maturity; rather, we have responded to circumstances entirely different from those immediately apparent.

I remember the first year I was pastor of the Wilmore Church. The county ministers took turns giving live devotions on a nearby radio station each morning. The fifteen-minute program started at 9:15. About every ten or twelve weeks it fell my turn. One day I was delayed in the office and rushed over to the radio station, arriving at 9:12 all out of breath. Three minutes later I gave the devotion.

After the program was over I walked out of the booth into the main office. The young secretary looked up at me and said, "Rev. Seamands, we like to have the speaker here at least ten minutes ahead of time, if you please." I remember my face getting flushed and my blurting out with a lot more emotion than I ever intended, "Well, I made it on time, didn't I?"

She looked a bit startled, but didn't answer because I was on my way out the door. I got in the car and drove to Wilmore by the back road. I was so upset I could hardly make it home. The whole way back I talked to myself: "Who in the world does that saucy little blonde think she is, anyhow? Doesn't she realize the busy schedule of a minister, how much time the program takes, how it ruins the morning? It takes a whole hour or more to come over here and do the broadcast."

I was practically ill before I got back to Wilmore. And then all of a sudden something dawned on me and I said to myself, "Seamands, what in the world has upset you like this?"

Now there is a good rule of thumb for measuring your reactions. When your response to a situation is way out of proportion to the event, you'd better suspect the little child within you is acting up.

With a surprising amount of feeling and emotion, a childhood experience was replayed in my mind, and I realized that I hadn't been talking to that impertinent little blonde in the radio station but reliving an incident from my childhood. All the feelings of a hurt little boy came out in that conversation.

When I saw it so clearly, I was able to ask the Holy Spirit to *katargeo* that particular incident, to move in and take the sting out of the memories, to render the experience null and void so that it would be no longer operative and active in my life. The next day I apologized to the young lady, to clear both my conscience and the atmosphere in the radio station.

## PERSONAL REFLECTION

■ The quantity of your birthdays may reveal your age in life, but the quality of behavior reveals your stage in life. Describe a time when your response to a situation was way out of proportion to what actually happened. What do you think was the real reason for your reaction?

_____

_____

_____

_____

_____

■ Have you ever thought about the difference between being *childlike* and acting *childish*? In column one below, list as many characteristics of *childlikeness* as you can think of. Then compile a list of *childish* characteristics in the second column. When you have finished putting your lists together, go back and with a highlighting pen highlight all the phrases from both columns that you feel generally describe you.

**Childlike Characteristics**     **Childish Characteristics**

_____     _____

_____     _____

_____     _____

_____     _____

_____     _____

_____     _____

_____     _____

_____     _____

_____     _____

■ Complete the following sentences:

*The people who seem to "push my buttons" most often are (list specific names)* _____

_____

_____

_____

_____

*The types of situations that most often get a strong reaction from me are*

_____

_____

_____

_____

_____

_____

_____

_____

■ Based on the answers you have written up to this point, what particular incidents or memories do you need the Holy Spirit to *katargeo*——render null and void—in your life? List them specifically and then, to the extent that you are able, entrust them to the tender care of the Holy Spirit.

_____

_____

_____

_____

I suppose the area of our lives where we most see the inner child is at home, especially in the intimacies of marriage. We make a mistake when we think that only two people marry. We say, "The two shall become one." That's fine, but the trouble is that four people marry, and sometimes things get crowded around the house. There are the two adults, and there are the two children of the past. It is perfectly all right as long as the adults are running things. But home is where we relax, where we let ourselves go and become again those little children of the past. Pretty soon that hidden inner child of the husband or of the wife wants to run the home, and that's when things get interesting. When all four start acting according to their differing family backgrounds, the fun really begins!

The chief areas where these four clash are money, affection, sex, and discipline of children. If this sounds farfetched to you, then you ought to hear a husband talking to me. With tears in his eyes he says, "I don't understand myself. I love my wife so much it hurts. And when I am at work all day, I say to myself, 'This evening is going to be different.' But when I get home, what happens? All the sweet, tender, loving things I've been practicing all day get stuck in my throat. When I walk in the door, all of a sudden I am just a frightened little boy again with Mom fussing at me. Instead of telling my wife I've missed her all day, I scold her about some fool thing. I start out to love her and I end up hurting her." Does that sound familiar?

Or maybe it's the wife who says, "You know, I'm all right until my husband begins to discipline the kids, and then I just can't stand it. I know that he isn't too hard on them. I know that I'm spoiling them and ruining them. I know they need to be spanked at times. But the minute he starts, I can see my dad all over again, and I end up fighting with my husband. I feel like a frightened little girl."

The great tragedy in all of this is that it keeps us from being free. It binds us to the past, chaining us to our childhood reactions. We are not free to love or to bring newness into our homes and into our relationships with people. We never really act, we just react. We merely respond, but seldom show creative love.

## PERSONAL REFLECTION

■ It is within the context of marriage, or other close relationships, that we most often see the inner child emerging in a conflictive way. What conflicts have you experienced with your spouse (or significant other) in the following areas that might be related to the "unfinished business" of your past? Be specific.

Money _____

_____

_____

_____

_____

_____

_____

Affection _____

_____

_____

_____

_____

Sex_____

_____

_____

_____

Discipline of children_____

_____

_____

_____

_____

Other key relational areas _____

_____

_____

■ To what extent do you feel you are still bound to the past? Abuse, be it verbal, emotional, physical, intellectual, sexual, or spiritual, is most often what keeps us tied to the past. What abuse are you aware of in your life that is rooted in the past? Name specific past abuses that you feel are still impacting your life today.

_____

_____

_____

_____

_____

_____

The Apostle Paul set his words about putting away childish things at the very heart and center of the great love chapter, 1 Corinthians 13. This perfect love which leads to maturity casts out fear and brings creativity and newness. But you can't find this kind of love and maturity until there is *katargeo*, until that hidden inner child of your past is dealt with.

The Holy Spirit will work in this area of your life if you give Him a chance, if you willingly surrender your pride and face yourself honestly. If this is what you want, spend some time alone asking Him to show you the truth about yourself and how you relate to other people. If you see recurring patterns of behavior which continually defeat you in your Christian life, then you'd better take an honest look at them.

That will not be easy. It is difficult to look in the mirror and admit, "I wasn't in control when I acted that way. A little child inside of me was in control." It may be so painful that you will need to go to a friend who can help you see yourself. Don't imagine problems if there are none. But don't be afraid to face them if they are real.

Every week I talk to people who profess wonderful Christian experiences but who are defeated in everyday areas of their lives which hurt their influence as Christians. God doesn't mean for any of us to go on living like this. He doesn't want us to continue in defeat. Rather, He wants to give us healing and wholeness, cleansing and victory. By the power of His Spirit, He wants to enable us to put away the inner child of our past and to grow up into Him in every way.

I'll never forget what one person said to me at the end of a counseling hour: "If what you say is true, then I have never really started living. I have to go back and be reborn and start all over again." You may need that kind of rebirth and release from the captivity of the inner child of your past. Thank God, this is His intention! Make it your intention too—whatever it may cost you.

**PRAYERFUL REFLECTION**

■ The pathway to healing and wholeness is, most often, a long one for those who choose to walk it. But the Holy Spirit, the Comforter, promises to walk alongside those who choose to travel this pathway. Are you ready to make the journey? Then, after speaking the prayer below aloud to God, sign your name at the end of it along with today's date.

*Blessed Holy Spirit,*
*I open myself to You. I will not hide behind the furniture*
*of my heart but come out into the open so that You may*
*show me myself. I pray, O Lord, that You will shine Your*
*light and reveal to me my inner self. Free me from the*
*chains which bind me to immaturity and childishness.*
*Prepare my heart for wholeness and fullness in Your*
*Spirit. Amen.*

_____

*YOUR SIGNATURE AND TODAY'S DATE*

**PERSONAL RENEWAL**

■ Set your heart on these words from the psalmist David as you begin your journey toward wholeness (Psalm 40:1-3, TLB):

*I waited patiently for God to help me; then He listened*
*and heard my cry. He lifted me out of the pit of despair,*
*out from the bog and the mire, and put my feet on a*
*hard, firm path, and steadied me as I walked along.*
*He has given me a new song to sing, of praises to*
*our God. Now many will hear of the glorious things*
*He did for me, and stand in awe before the Lord,*
*and put their trust in Him.*

*Simon Peter was following Jesus, and so was another disciple. Now that disciple was known to the high priest, and entered with Jesus into the court of the high priest, but Peter was standing at the door outside. . . .The slave-girl therefore who kept the door said to Peter, "You are not also one of this man's disciples, are you?" He said, "I am not."*

*Now the slaves and the officers were standing there, having made a charcoal fire, for it was cold and they were warming themselves; and Peter also was with them, standing and warming himself. . . .*

*They said therefore to him, "You are not also one of His disciples, are you?" He denied it, and said, "I am not." One of the slaves of the high priest, being a relative of the one whose ear Peter cut off, said, "Did I not see you in the garden with Him?" Peter therefore denied it again; and immediately a cock crowed.*

*But the other disciples came in the little boat, for they were not far from the land, but about one hundred yards away, dragging the net full of fish. And so when they got out upon the land, they saw a charcoal fire already laid, and fish placed on it, and bread. . . .*

*Jesus said to them, "Come and have breakfast."*

*So when they had finished breakfast, Jesus said to Simon Peter, "Simon, son of John, do you love Me more than these?" . . . He said to him again a second time, "Simon, son of John, do you love me?" . . . He said to him the third time, "Simon, son of John, do you love Me?"*

*Peter was grieved because He said to him the third time, "Do you love Me" and he said to Him, "Lord, You know all things; You know that I love You."*

*John 18:15-18, 25-27; 21:8-9, 12, 15-17*

# Chapter 2
# The Healing of Memories

I remember that Sunday evening service in 1966 when with great fear and hesitation I preached on the theme, "The Holy Spirit and the Healing of Our Damaged Emotions." I doubt if I have preached another sermon which God has seen fit to use as much as that one. The tapes have gone all over the world and have been the means of bringing release to people held captive by their emotions.

In 1967 I received a letter from a lady who somehow got the idea that I had written a book by that title. In her letter she said, "Dear Dr. Seamands: Please send me your Damaged Emotions." I would like to have done that, but I figured she had enough of her own without taking on mine! In 1981 my book *Healing for Damaged Emotions* was published, and I hope the lady has a copy.

As far as I can discover, the phrase "the healing of the memories" began with Agnes Sanford, an amazing Episcopalian lady who God has used so miraculously in a healing ministry all around the world. The term is hers, but the basic idea is an old one which has long been used by Christian counselors and psychologists. If I use some terms and ideas that you have read in other books, I do not apologize. God seems to have impressed this theme on many of us at about the same time. Besides, there is an old saying that if you use one person's ideas, that's plagiarism; but if you use two, that's research!

I am neither a professional theologian nor a psychiatrist. I call myself a pastor-evangelist and counselor. I can't give you all the technical answers about the relationship between original sin and damaged emotions. Nor can I give you the exact distinction between the carnal mind and disturbed emotions. One time after hearing me preach on the inner child of the past, a parishioner kidded me: "David, all this time I've heard it was the 'old man,' and now you're saying it is a 'little child' within me causing the problem."

I don't have all the exact theological answers at this point. But I do know that as I read the theologians and the biographies of the saints, and as I honestly reflect on my own spiritual autobiography, I see plenty of imperfections in the perfect. Conversely, there can be purity of intention within imperfect expression. King David prayed: "Who can understand his errors? Cleanse Thou me from secret faults. Keep back Thy servant also from presumptuous sins; let them not have dominion over me; then shall I be upright, and I shall be innocent from the great transgression" (Psalm 19:12-13, KJV).

The obvious place to begin with this troublesome inner child of the past is where he really makes himself felt—in our memories. It might be tempting to go off on a high-sounding tangent to discuss the unconscious mind, but personally, I think we have overdone this a bit. At most, I like to talk about the subconscious mind or perhaps a preconscious mind.

## PERSONAL REFLECTION

- Scientists tell us that the average brain weighs about three pounds and consists of roughly three trillion brain cell connections. Dr. Gehard Dirks, one of the chief developers of the IBM computer, commented, "If we could invent a computer that would duplicate the capabilities of the human brain, it would take a structure the size of the Empire State Building, just to house it" (*The Battle for the Mind*, Tim LaHaye, Revell, p. 13). What do you think of when you hear the phrase "subconscious" or "preconscious" mind? Based on your impression of Dr. Dirk's observation about the brain, how do you feel about the capacity of your own mind to store memories from the past?

  _____

  _____

  _____

- Damaged emotions that are stored in your memory hold you captive to the past. Do you believe this statement? Why or why not?

  _____

  _____

  _____

I think the reason for overemphasis on the unconscious is to find an excuse, an escape from responsibility for our own wrong behavior. If you still prefer the term, remember that the unconscious is not an entity, not a thing. Unconscious is a descriptive word attempting to portray the depths of your personality. Whatever you call the subconscious level of you mind, the fact is that you never forget anything you experience. Although you may not be able to recall it at will, anything that ever crossed your path lives in your memory. It is filed in the storeroom of your mind. This is both wonderful and terrible. It is both the misery and the grandeur of being a human.

## PERSONAL REFLECTION

■ Have you ever had a dream that brought back a memory you had pushed out of your mind for many years? Or have you had an experience in the present—heard, seen, or done something—that sent you skyrocketing back to an experience you had in the distant past? Describe it.

_____

_____

_____

If you let the Holy Spirit reach down deep, cleanse your subconscious mind, and get into the depths of your heart to fill the storehouse of memory, God will give you power to actually make this one of the most creative parts of your personality.

Long ago I discovered the amazing power of the subconscious part of my mind in helping me prepare sermons. I have found that if weeks and months in advance, I feed certain basic ideas deep into my mind—a title, a brief outline, some thought of what I want to say—then the preacher doesn't simply work on the sermon. The sermon also works on the preacher! My subconscious mind is always occupied with that sermon, even when I'm busy with other duties. You probably have a busy life where time is scarce. If you feed ideas into your mind, it will work on them for you. Then when you are ready, so is what you need, as a product of the great power of this deep level of mind and memory.

One night in October 1920, in Toronto, Canada, Dr. Frederick G. Banting was working on his lecture for the following day. He was a young surgeon with such a small professional practice that he had to teach in order to make a living. For several hours Banting studied the literature on diabetes. It was scant for at that time medical science offered no means of control for the dreaded disease. Banting's mind was a maze of conflicting theories and accounts of experiments with dogs.

At a late hour he went wearily to bed, only to be suddenly awakened at two in the morning. His subconscious mind had some ideas to offer. He got up and wrote down three short sentences in his notebook and then went back to sleep. Those three sentences led to the discovery of insulin. Banting's subconscious mind had come up with the solution when his conscious mind had found none. It was his subconscious mind which brought hope and life to millions of suffering people.

## PERSONAL REFLECTION

■ In the previous four paragraphs, Dr. Seamands shows how the subconscious mind can be a tremendous source of creative and positive power. Can you think of a time when your subconscious mind came up with a creative or constructive solution to an impending problem? Describe it.

_____

_____

_____

_____

_____

_____

_____

The subconscious mind can also be a tormenter, for it contains tremendous power for producing evil and misery. This especially relates to painful childhood memories. In trying to push them out of our minds, we actually bury them deeper and deeper, until they no longer can find a way out. As a result, the intense emotions we experienced but did not express at the time the hurt occurred, have no way of being expressed now. Buried alive within our hearts, they retain amazing persistence and explosive power.

While we may think we are free of those apparently forgotten torments, this is not the case, for submerged memories cannot be stored away in peace in the same way that the mind files pleasant memories. Instead, we have to keep closing the door again and again, refusing to let these painful memories into our conscious minds. Since they can't enter through the door of our minds, they disguise themselves and try to smuggle into our personalities through another door.

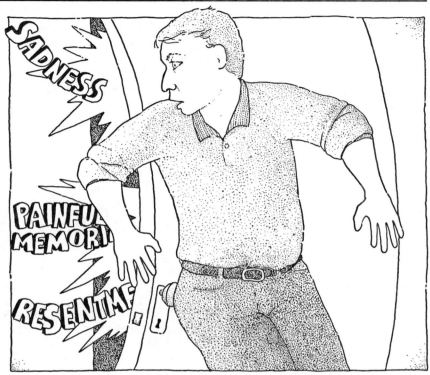

The great effort required to keep these memories below the surface of the conscious mind is a constant drag on our energy. Some of us are as tired when we get up in the morning as when we went to bed at night, even though we have had eight hours of sleep. Why? All night long the battle has been raging in the depth of our personalities, causing a constant drain on our energies.

Many people live with the unresolved tensions of painful memories for years, during which the load increases. If such a person comes to the end of his endurance and finds his energies depleted, he becomes a prime candidate for an emotional crisis. If he is further weakened by physical exhaustion, illness, or traumatic shock, and then if some experience takes place which associates itself with a painful event of the past, those hidden memories he has so long tried to bury are awakened and reactivated.

When the dormant inner child of the past is thus aroused, he can take over the person's attitudes, reactions, outlook, and behavior. The submerged emotions rise up and express themselves in feelings of deep depression, rage, uncontrollable lust, inferiority, fear, loneliness, and rejection.

## PERSONAL REFLECTION

■ What painful memories or feelings have you "buried alive" in your subconscious mind? How have those submerged memories and emotions emerged in your life at unexpected times or in self-destructive ways? Describe some ways.

_____

_____

_____

_____

_____

_____

_____

_____

These painful memories are not automatically evicted or transformed by an experience of conversion or even by the filling of the Holy Spirit. They are not necessarily changed by growth in grace. In fact, these memories are often great hindrances to spiritual growth. And until a person receives deliverance from them, he does not really mature. It is as if one part of his person is in a deep freeze, or in a time machine. His body matures and his mind develops but that one particular area is still frozen. He remains a little boy, she is still a little girl, locked into that childhood stage of life.

Unfortunately, these memories do not seem to be reached by our ordinary levels of prayer. Sometimes prayer seems to make the pain even worse. You feel you are in quicksand: the more you fight and struggle, the deeper you sink.

I believe this situation calls for a special kind of shared praying and healing. The confusing thing is that often there is nothing wrong with the person in his present life. Not understanding this, Christian friends have been known to berate such people by saying, "There is sin in your life." Or, "You are guilty of some transgression."

Such people are made to feel guilty about disobedience to God, when just the opposite may be true. Sometimes they are the finest, most sincere Christians who are trying the hardest. They read and pray and struggle with their hangups. Their friends give them Scripture verses, books, and lots of advice. All this only adds to their agony, so they become disillusioned and sometimes despair of life.

Please don't berate a person like this! There is nothing wrong with his present adult mind. His commitment to Christ is clear, his surrender as complete as he knows how to make it. The trouble is in the child he used to be, who still lives within him, repressed and crushed down into the mind, and unexpressed until something causes it to rise up and take over.

## PERSONAL REFLECTION

■ In what ways do you identify with what Dr. Seamands writes in the previous three paragraphs? Have you ever been told by "well-meaning" Christians that your emotional struggle was really just a spiritual problem? Have they tried to apply a spiritual "quick fix" to your emotional pain or expressed struggle? Describe how your inner child responded to the "quick fix" solution offered.

_____

_____

_____

_____

_____

_____

■ James 5:16a says, "Admit your faults to one another and pray for each other so that you may be healed" (TLB). What do you think this verse means? Is this a verse you would feel comfortable doing with other people in your church? Why or why not?

_____

_____

_____

_____

_____

■ Are you aware of any ways in which your spiritual growth has been stunted because of unresolved painful memories from the past? What part of your relationship with God seems to cause you the most grief?

_____

_____

_____

_____

Often what is required in situations of this kind is prayer for the healing of memories—the healing of that little child or teenager who underwent certain experiences which made him stop growing, experiences which imprisoned him, froze him at one stage in his growth. All those memories need to be offered to God in a prayer for healing, so that the person can be freed from his pain and compulsion.

You may ask, "What happens then? Will he no longer remember? Will the memories be erased?" Certainly not! But the power of the emotions which surround those memories—the sting, the pain, the fear, the hate, the hurt, the lust—will be broken. As we *katargeo* them, they will lose their propulsive significance. They will be devitalized, no longer effective and operative in the adult life.

So, you may ask, "How is this possible? After all, those childhood experiences are gone. They took place many, many years ago. How can our prayers today possibly affect that inner child of the long-ago past? It doesn't make sense." To which I reply, in the words of Jesus, "You are mistaken, not understanding the Scriptures, or the power of God" (Matthew 22:29).

For you see, Scripture over and over again emphasizes that Jesus Christ transcends time. "Jesus Christ is the same yesterday and today, yes and forever" (Hebrews 13:8). John the Baptist, talking about Jesus, said, "Here is the One I was speaking about when I said that although He would come after me He would always be in front of me; for He existed before I was born!" (John 1:15, PH) The Jews mockingly said to Jesus one day, "'You are not yet fifty years old, and have you seen Abraham?' Jesus said to them, 'Truly, truly, I say to you, before Abraham was, I am'" (John 8:57-58, RSV).

Jesus of Nazareth is the everlasting Christ who broke through the time barrier and entered history. He lived within our time for thirty-three earthly years. But time is a finite concept. It is the way you and I experience reality—in pieces, in parts. We divide time into past, present, and future. But Christ transcends all of time. "Even from everlasting to everlasting, Thou art God . . . for a thousand years in Thy sight are like yesterday when it passes by" (Psalm 90:2, 4).

Thus our Lord is not restricted by time. He is our eternal contemporary who can walk back through time to minister to that hurting little child. Jesus can gather him into His loving arms, comforting and loving that child who so desperately wanted to be loved but never was. He can understand that little child who so intensely sought to be understood, but never was. He can reassure that child with the unconditional, accepting love he so acutely needed but never experienced. He can forgive that guilty, shame-filled little child the way he so deeply wanted to be forgiven back then, encouraging him and replacing the feelings of condemnation and dirtiness with virtue and cleanness. Yes, Jesus, the tender and everlasting Shepherd, can gather the lambs into His arms and heal their tormented, thorn-filled memories.

## PERSONAL REFLECTION

■ STOP! Go back and reread the previous paragraph again . . . and again . . . and again. Can you picture, in your mind's eye, Jesus as He is described there? Turn to the next page and in the space provided, draw a picture of yourself with Jesus. Make your drawing as simple or as detailed as you like. Use conversation balloons to express anything you want to say to Jesus or long to hear Him say to you. If you feel hesitant about doing this art exercise, stop for a moment and ask the Holy Spirit who tenderly comforts and guides to help you do what you can.

My experience is that the inner child of the past which most needs healing is usually one of four kinds: he is the *hurting* child, the *hating* child, the *humiliated* child, or the *horrified* child. The memories that seem to grip and grind us, that have an almost hypnotic sway and power over us, are memories of deep emotional pain, resentment, hate, fear, or embarrassment. Sometimes it is a mixture of all these.

With increasing frequency, some form of sexual abuse is mingled with the memories—violation, homosexuality, betrayal, or incest. And so some people, who in their present lives are very sincere Christians, experience a near hypnotic, propulsive, and compulsive lust in their lives. Their imaginations paint terrible pictures on the walls of their minds, driving them into guilt and depression, and almost to self-destructive actions. Or, they have a deep-seated distrust and revulsion toward sex which prevents them from having meaningful relationships with their spouses.

I want to share a couple of experiences I have had with people who, in prayer, experienced a healing of the memories.

### Mike's Story

Mike was a committed Christian, a leader among youth, a dedicated Sunday School teacher who was much loved by all his students. Yet he had a deep inner struggle in his spiritual life—he could never quite believe that God loved him. Every once in a while, strong feelings of rage, bitterness, and lust would get hold of Mike. These would be followed by guilt, depression, and a feeling that God had forsaken him and was far away.

We counseled together several times and tried all the ordinary ways of praying, but there was no real deliverance. One day I explained to Mike the concept of the healing of memories. I loaned him some books and tapes and asked him to write down the most troublesome and hurtful memories that came to mind as he read and listened.

Finally, when I thought he was ready for this special time of prayer, we met for an undisturbed and unhurried time of openness to the Holy Spirit. We entered into an open, conversational kind of prayer in which we just talked to each other and to God, remembering that He was right there in the room.

As we did this, several pictures arose in Mike's mind, one which was a very binding, grinding, and searing scene. This memory was central to his childhood, so dominant that he still had repeated nightmares about the event. Mike's father was well-meaning and sincere, but a very harsh disciplinarian. To punish Mike whenever he did any childish wrong, his father would shut him up inside a little room in the barn. There he would strap him severely until Mike was screaming for mercy, crying for his mother and his brothers and sisters to come and let him out. He'd run for the door of the barn, but his father would get there first and stand at the door barring the way. He would then order Mike, "Say you're sorry." He would repeat this over and over again, until the hysterical little boy would finally say he was sorry. Then his father would force Mike to embrace and kiss him.

As we prayed together and as Mike began to bring this memory to the Lord in prayer, he started to relive the emotion of it! All the resentment, hurt, and terrifying fear came into his voice. I didn't know what to say or how to pray, so I just waited on the Spirit for guidance, asking Him to pray in me and through me.

All of a sudden it came to me. As I was praying, I saw little Mike. We were confined together in that horrible barn. And I realized that emotionally Mike was still in the barn, that he had never gotten outside the door. He had lived in that barn for fifteen years without getting around his father and out of the door. Inside himself he was still screaming, still hysterical with fear, still burning with rage.

When I began to pray, I believe it was in the spirit of Romans 8:26-27, where we are told the Holy Spirit Himself intercedes for us.

"Lord Jesus, we are in the barn together. Take this little boy in Your arms, dry his tears, quiet his fears, cleanse away his hate. But, O Lord, above all, open the door and let him out."

When I said that, he began to sob uncontrollably. I continued, "Lord, Mike has never seen the blue sky. He has never lived in Your love and freedom. He is still locked in the barn. Open the door now, and let him out—set him free!"

While we were praying, it happened. It seemed as though Jesus rolled back the carpet of time and walked right into that barn. He took frightened little Mike in His arms and comforted him, loved him, and healed him. All the scars and the wounds were washed with the Balm of Gilead. Then we saw the door opening and Jesus taking that frightened, hurt, hate-filled lad out of the barn and into the clear sky and clean air of God's love.

### Anne's Story

I used to wonder along with Nicodemus who asked, "Can a man really be born all over again when he gets old?" New birth for young people we can understand—it seems much simpler for them. But let me tell you about Anne, a married woman in her mid-forties, who came to see me after one of my meetings. She had several teenage children. Her marriage was about to break up because of her terrible inner conflicts and the way she was taking them out on her family. As we counseled together, I saw that she was a deeply sincere woman who had spent many hours praying about her problem. We talked several times and I loaned her some books to read. These helped her to open up and share with me many things she had never before talked about.

When I thought Anne was ready, we had our time of healing prayer together. She lifted up to God her awful childhood and teenage memories. She had an abusive alcoholic father who made sexual advances toward her, broke up the home, and then committed suicide.

We prayed for the deepest possible healing of those childhood memories and the cleansing of all her twisted emotions. Nothing seemed to happen when we prayed together. I didn't see her for about two weeks. Then she told me this most amazing story, and we knew God had answered our prayers.

It happened this way: about a week after we had prayed, she awoke very early one morning. She couldn't get back to sleep so she lay in bed and began to pray. She said it was as if Christ Himself came into the bedroom, called her and said, "Come, Anne, take My hand. I want us to walk back through your life."

"Lord, I couldn't stand it again. It was so hard when I told the pastor."

"Anne, this time is going to be different. I am going to be with you each step of the way."

Anne then described that walk with Jesus in a most unusual fashion. The two of them were in a great art gallery where each painful incident was a picture on the wall. As Jesus led her they would stand before each vivid memory, like looking at a painting. And as she looked at them one by one, all the original emotions she had experienced swept over her. Once more she relived the fear, the pain, the shame, and the rage connected with those ghastly memories. Each time she would weep bitter tears and each time an inner voice would say, "My child, just turn it over to Me; forgive everyone involved and receive forgiveness for your own hate and rage." As she surrendered each memory to the Lord, it was as if Jesus reached up and took down that particular picture.

This went on for several hours until finally, when she looked around, all the pictures had been taken down and the walls of her mind were clean and whole. The scalding bitterness and the poisonous fangs had been removed from those destructive memories.

That dramatic experience was many years ago and, although there was a lot of reprogramming which had to be done as a follow-up, it was clearly the beginning of her healing. A subsequent medical and psychiatric report confirmed this. Her deliverance and transformation has been a source of joy to her husband and family and to those who work with her.

Both Mike and Anne needed healing for childhood and teenage memories. However, many times the painful memory is more recent, a part of an adult life. This is especially true of some of the traumas surrounding our modern tragedies involving sex, violence, and the sense of betrayal in a divorce. The same principles apply and bring about release and healing when often the more ordinary means of prayer do not. The best biblical example of this is the way Jesus handled Peter's denial and restoration.

These are the only two places in the New Testament where the word for "a charcoal fire" is used. Surely this is more than coincidence. It is obvious that Jesus deliberately set the stage for His conversation with Peter on the beach that post-Resurrection morning. Peter had denied Him three times while standing near a charcoal fire in the high priest's courtyard. Now he would be asked to affirm his love and loyalty three times. Everyone knows this part, but the fact that Jesus staged the conversation by asking Peter to relive the very setting of his denial seems to be overlooked. Surely the memory of those courtyard coals had been burning like fire in the conscience and memory of Peter. Here the Master Psychiatrist led Peter to face his most traumatic memory, and used a charcoal fire to cauterize and heal Peter's pain and shame. With the sting removed, Peter would be able to use that burning memory not as a curse which crippled, but as a spark to ignite him to an even deeper devotion, even unto death!

## PERSONAL REFLECTION

■ With which of the three stories—Mike's, Anne's, Peter's—do you most closely identify? Why?

_____

_____

_____

_____

■ Express how you feel about the use of prayer in the healing of memories. Have you ever had a prayer experience similar to Mike's with a pastor-counselor or Christian therapist? Describe it. What was the result of that prayer in your life? If you have never experienced the type of healing prayer Dr. Seamands describes in the previous accounts, would you like to? Why or why not?

_____

_____

_____

_____

_____

_____

_____

■ In what ways have you, like Anne, walked back through the halls of time to view your own "gallery" of painful memories? Where was God in the process? How did your experience strengthen your sense of relationship with God?

_____

_____

_____

_____

_____

I know this may all sound much too simple—like a shortcut. It is not meant to be a cure-all; this type of healing prayer doesn't apply to everybody. However, it does apply to some. The difference is perhaps largely a difference of degree in our lives. I am trusting the Holy Spirit will apply it to those who need this deeper kind of healing experience.

While this experience can take place when you are by yourself, it doesn't usually happen that way. I believe it is the kind of healing spoken about by James in his epistle. "Confess your sins to one another, and pray for one another, so that you may be healed. The effective prayer of a righteous man can accomplish much" (5:16). Healing of the memories usually requires a very deep openness and sharing with another person, and then the prayer of faith by that other person for you on your behalf. You see, you are so intricately involved in the whole matter that you may be unable to reach the inner layers of the child of your past.

You should spend time preparing yourself and reaching an openness to the Holy Spirit for new insights and the courage to surrender your defenses. This kind of praying should take place with someone you trust and respect, and whom you believe can pray the prayer of faith on your behalf.

It is often helpful to write out a list of the areas in your life that need to be cleansed and healed—anything that rises to bother you or memories that have powerful emotional overtones. Omit nothing, however insignificant, petty, or even foolish it may seem, as you open your heart to the probing scalpel of the Holy Spirit. Don't be surprised at what comes to your mind.

Paul Tournier says this inward examination is like entering a dark room. At first your eyes see only the most evident and the prominent objects, and you say, "Oh, there's only a table and a chair." But as your eyes become more accustomed to the dark you begin to realize the whole room is filled with an amazing clutter of objects. Don't be afraid. Relax in the Spirit. Thank Him for every new insight, however painful.

Pray with someone in whom you have confidence, one who knows how to really pray the prayer of faith. Conversational prayer together with that person and with the Lord is easiest and best. Confess to God every feeling, every emotion you experience as you relate these memories. If you remember anything new, interrupt and share it at once, for it is the Spirit taking you to a deeper level of your mind that may need healing.

Remember that Christ is alive. He is here now. And because He transcends time, He is also back at that painful experience. Confess to Him, turn over to Him each experience, each emotion, each attitude. Let Him love and comfort and forgive you. Let Him cleanse your hates and comfort your hurts and disinfect your lusts and remove your fears. Then specifically forgive others their trespasses as He also forgives you. Let Christ's love take the place of hate. Let Christ's strength take the place of hurt feelings and self-pity. Don't be in a hurry. Allow plenty of time for undisturbed, unhurried prayer.

If you are the one who is praying the prayer of faith for others, let the Holy Spirit melt your spirit with theirs. This is not easy work. Baron von Hugel talked about the "neural cost of intercessory prayer." Such prayer is demanding and exhausting. Let the Lord fill you with understanding and empathy so you can feel the same sorrow, anger, hurt, and fear. In this way the Spirit can pray through you, putting the very words in your mouth. If the Spirit leads you in the spirit of James 5, lay hands on them, even anoint them with oil. Prayerfully and carefully obey the Spirit without embarrassment or fear. Your feelings at the time are not as important as your trusting faith.

Your friend may not have much faith, so you may need to have enough faith for both of you! It was when the four disciples let the paralyzed man down through the roof before Jesus that He saw their faith and healed the man (Luke 5:19-20). Jesus said to Jairus about his sick daughter, "Don't be afraid; just believe, and she will be healed" (Luke 8:50, NIV). In these and other instances, faith on behalf of another brought healing.

Finally, don't dictate to the Holy Spirit how He is to accomplish His work. It may take several prayers, as the Spirit peels away a layer at a time. It may happen on the spot in a great rush of victory and release. It may come about several days or even weeks later. It may happen by leading that person to another healing experience . . . never mind, God will answer the prayer of faith for that person.

## PRAYERFUL REFLECTION

■ The prayer experience Dr. Seamands describes in this chapter is not a "cure-all" or "quick fix" to the healing process God has mapped out for you. While healing prayer does apply to *some*, it does not necessarily apply to *everybody*. Emotional healing, for most people, is a long and painful process. If, however, in the course of your own healing journey, you have come to a crossroads and want to experience God's healing touch in a greater way than you have up to this point, then you may want to prepare yourself for a new leg of your journey that includes healing prayer. Here are some steps you can take to prepare yourself for this type of prayer experience:

1. Humbly ask God to show you whether or not you are ready for an experience of this kind.

2. Spend time preparing yourself by staying open to new insights the Holy Spirit gives you; surrender your self-protective defenses to Him.

3. Write down a list of areas in your life that need to be cleansed and healed. (Step Four of the Twelve Steps talks about doing "a fearless, moral inventory.")

4. Relax in the Spirit. Trust Him to guide. Thank Him for any new insights He gives you.

5. Ask God to bring someone into your life who knows how to really pray the prayer of faith. Spend time getting to know that person so you feel safe and have a sense of confidence in him or her.

6. Trust the Holy Spirit to guide you through the healing process at His pace. He will never force you to move forward against your will; He will wait until you are ready.

■ Write a prayer expressing to God any fears or reservations you feel concerning experiencing healing prayer at a personal level. Nothing you say to Him will offend or surprise Him. Just be as honest and direct with Him as you can be at this moment.

_____

_____

_____

_____

_____

_____

## PERSONAL RENEWAL

■ When trust has been broken in our human relationships, we often find it difficult to trust an "invisible" God. Healing prayer begins with TRUST. This week, open up your heart to new possibilities as you read and reflect on three verses that describe a God who is perfectly trustworthy.

*And the Lord is the One who goes ahead of you; He will be with you. He will not fail you or forsake you. Do not fear, or be dismayed.*

*Deuteronomy 31:8*

*Call to Me, and I will answer you, and I will tell you great and mighty things, which you do not know.*

*Jeremiah 33:3*

*The Lord is near to all who call upon Him, to all who call upon Him in truth.*

*Psalm 145:18*

*There is therefore now no condemnation for those who are in Christ Jesus. For the law of the Spirit of life in Christ Jesus has set you free from the law of sin and of death.*

*What then shall we say to these things? If God is for us, who is against us? He who did not spare His own Son, but delivered Him up for us all, how will He not also with Him freely give us all things? Who will bring a charge against God's elect? God is the One who justifies; who is the one who condemns? Christ Jesus is He who died, yes, rather who was raised, who is at the right hand of God, who also intercedes for us.*

*Romans 8:1-2, 31-34*

# Chapter 3
# A Childhood Motto
# Which Destroys Adults

A few years ago I attended a Holy Spirit Conference in Michigan. One day a pastor named Brad shared with us that for many years he had been a struggling, up-and-down Christian. Outwardly he was a very successful pastor with a record of considerable accomplishments. But inwardly he was like a yo-yo, bouncing between spiritual highs and lows. Or like a billiard ball batting from one side to another, hitting pride on one side and condemnation, guilt, and depression on the other.

Brad told us, "A couple of years ago, there came to me a flash of insight from the Holy Spirit. I suddenly realized that my life was not really being ruled by love for God and for other people. Instead, for the past forty-nine years a little childhood motto instilled in me by my parents had really been running my life. All those years I thought Christ controlled my life, until I became aware that it was a motto I had adopted in my early years." What was the powerful childhood motto? "Measure up!" Brad continued, "I'm sure my parents didn't mean to give me this impression, but what I heard them saying was, "Sure we love you, but we would love you more if only you would measure up!"

PERSONAL
REFLECTION

■ Describe what your spiritual walk with God has looked like over the past six months. Use a few tell-tale phrases to describe it, OR chart it in a graph-like grid using the lines on the next page.

_____

_____

_____

_____

_____

■ What would you say your spiritual life has most been influenced by in the last six months? In what ways, if any, do you relate to Brad's statement, "I suddenly realized that my life was not really being ruled by love for God and other people. Instead, for the past forty-nine years a little childhood motto instilled in me by my parents had really been running my life"?

_____

_____

_____

_____

The Holy Spirit began to help Brad look at himself and see the real motivation of his life. He realized that those two simple words, carried over from his childhood, were affecting him in all his present relationships, including his relationship with God. For forty-nine years he had never felt he could measure up. "But now at last I am gaining freedom from that childhood motto and am learning true freedom in the Holy Spirit."

An amazingly accurate diagnosis of some people! Instead of living by the wonderful good news of the Gospel, they are living by the directives of some childhood motto. Some of them are experts at declaring the biblical truth, but their lives are actually directed by a motto which dictates the opposite of the truth they are declaring. They confess Christ, but are controlled by an immature motto or vow.

Does a childhood motto rule your life? The Apostle Paul said that true sons and daughters of God are led and controlled by the Holy Spirit (Romans 8:9, 14). Does the Holy Spirit control and direct your life? Or is it an immature, childish spirit from your past? Or maybe it is a combination. The two can get so tangled up that you don't discern the difference. What you may think is the voice of God, may really be the voice of an immature conscience lashing you into a sense of guilt, driving you under the tyranny of self-condemnation. Sometimes this doesn't change in conversion, nor even in being filled with the Spirit.

Let's look at Brad's motto. Brad was being controlled by a God who seemed to be constantly saying, "Measure up." But this is not the God who has been shown to us in Jesus Christ. This is not God at all. Rather, it is a childhood motto which became his god and ruled him as a ruthless dictator.

You see, this is the God of the immature, childish, and neurotic perfectionist. It is not the God of the mature Christian, who by faith is receiving the perfection of Jesus Christ, so that perfection is no longer the attainment of perfect performance, but rather the gift of a right relationship with God.

Relationship? But that is exactly where this childhood motto perverts God's plan of salvation. On this deadly perfectionist path to salvation, God is an increasingly demanding tyrant. He is like Pharaoh who first says, "Make more bricks," and then demands, "Now make them without straw." He always wants a little more. He's never quite pleased with me as I am today, but always says, "You could have done better than that." The God of this motto is not the Father-God revealed to us by Jesus Christ. He is more like the godfather of the Mafia. Measure up! Perform—or else.

## PERSONAL REFLECTION

■ What childhood mottos most influence your life today, perhaps wreaking havoc in your relationships, including your relationship with God? Name the childhood mottos from your past that continue to influence your life in the present. *EXAMPLES: Only weak people cry. If you'd just exercise a little more self-control, you'd be able to overcome that awful habit.*

_____

_____

_____

_____

_____

■ In his book, *Tired of Trying to Measure Up*, Jeff VanVonderen states that "Most modern approaches to understanding ourselves and making changes in our lives focus on the central ingredient of effort. Whether our problem is doing something we wish we weren't doing, or wanting to completely surrender our life to God, or struggling to believe God really loves us, the line is still the same: Try harder!" (Bethany House, p. 139) Are you caught in a "try-harder" cycle of spirituality? Describe what your "try-harder" cycle looks like at present.

_____

_____

_____

_____

_____

■ How do you know the voice of God in your life? Have you ever felt confused about whether it is the Holy Spirit talking to you or merely an immature conscience lashing out at you in a condemning way? Describe a time when you felt confused by what you "heard" God saying to you.

_____

_____

_____

_____

_____

■ What type of God do you have? Describe Him as you know Him today. (How do you *experience* God in your heart—not just *know* Him in your head?)

_____

_____

_____

_____

_____

The tragedy is that so much of this occurs in our homes, even in the best of them. We are all sinners, and at no place are we in more need of God's unconditional grace than in our roles as parents. Our love is so imperfect, so conditional, so varying, so full of flaws. And there are times when the conditionality is even made worse because we are so zealous to bring up our children as good Christians.

I have a young friend named Bob. When he was a child, the "Measure-up" motto was built into him by his parents. He thought it was the basis for his being loved and accepted. And since he needed to feel accepted and loved, he tried to please his parents. But they were like we all are at times. So subtly we withhold our full affection and love until we see that our children are striving at their highest level. Instead of affirming them where they are, we "encourage" them to "do a little bit better." So whatever they do—eating their food or using good manners or making grades or living the Christian life on their own age level—we give our children the promise of our approval and love if only they will do a little bit better. Love becomes something just around the corner, just a hope away. The present level of achievement is subtly downgraded and belittled. We think we are saying, "We love you and want you to do better." Too often it comes across to our children as, "We will love you when you measure up," or "We will love you and be pleased with you, if only you'll do a little bit better."

This whole system of conditional relationships and attitudes was built right into Bob. And this was why, even after he grew up and realized great success in his work, he never felt he had accomplished anything. He was never satisfied, but was always belittling his own efforts. He couldn't accept a compliment graciously. When a friend complimented him, he'd explain it away. After all, he really could have done better. He felt he never achieved sufficiently to merit approval and love.

Tragically, this all became a part of Bob's Christianity. And oh, how hard he worked to satisfy his built-in Pharaoh with a lash, who kept him running faster and faster on a terrible treadmill. Striving, trying, reaching, but never quite making it. Reading more and more books on the deeper life, attending one more revival or retreat, one more trip to the altar to be fully sanctified (the very same reason he went to the altar the last time). His was an "if-only-I-could" Christian life. But nothing quite worked, and when he fell off spiritual cloud nine with a thud, a little inner voice always scolded him with, "Measure up—that's not quite good enough."

## PERSONAL REFLECTION

■ How was love expressed in the family in which you grew up?

_____

_____

_____

_____

■ Rich Buhler in his book, *Love: No Strings Attached*, discusses the difference between *love* and *approval*. He says that "*approval* must be earned and is granted because of what a person does. Approval has to do with 'doing.' Approval can be lost" (Nelson, p. 27). Describe a time when you lost the approval of someone who was important to you. How did you feel when you lost that person's approval?

_____

_____

_____

_____

■ Who are the people in your life from whom you have most often sought approval, perhaps thinking that if they approved of you, you would feel loved by them? Name specific individuals and describe things you have done in the past to win their approval.

_____

_____

_____

_____

_____

■ Many people withhold love as a way of expressing disapproval. (Remember that approval has to do with doing.) Think of a time when a significant other withheld love from you as a means of expressing disapproval toward you for something you did that made him or her unhappy. How has that experience impacted you emotionally? Spiritually? Have you ever withheld love as a means of expressing disapproval? When? Why?

_____

_____

_____

_____

_____

■ There are no strings attached to unconditional love. Give an example from your life of being *conditionally* loved. What did it cost you to get that love? Then cite an example of someone loving you *unconditionally*.

_____

_____

_____

_____

_____

Jesus told of a loving Father who delights to give good gifts to His children, especially His gift of the Holy Spirit (Matthew 7:11 and Luke 11:13). Bob had reversed that so while he kept seeking, he never found. He asked but he never received. He knocked so loudly his knuckles were bloody, but all he got back was the echo of knocking himself, in his self-belittling and self-berating. And the door never seemed to open for him, for the inevitable consequences of "Measure up" are an unpleasable God and a Gospel which is a grinding demand instead of a gracious offer.

There is no doubt that this motto, "Measure up," camouflages and sabotages true Christian holiness more than any other. For the essence of holiness is love—deep, pure, mature love for God, for others, and for myself. The whole "Measure up" system short-circuits love at every one of those three key points: God, others, and self. It offers you a kind of God you can't possibly love. So you end up resenting and resisting Him, like the elder brother who served his father all those many years, but with deep resentment (Luke 15:25-32). Without proper self-esteem and love you can't love your neighbor. Instead you will end up resenting your neighbor just as much as you resent yourself.

## PERSONAL REFLECTION

■ In the previous paragraph Dr. Seamands states, "...this motto, "Measure up," camouflages and sabotages true Christian holiness more than any other." Has this been your experience? How have your valiant attempts at "doing right" gotten in the way of your "knowing God and His grace"?

_____

_____

_____

_____

_____

■ Do you ever feel resentful toward God and/or other people because all your efforts of trying to "Measure up" never seem to be quite enough? Why do you think you try so hard and feel so resentful?

_____

_____

_____

_____

_____

Again and again I am asked, "But how is all this possible in the life of a truly born-again and Spirit-filled Christian? Surely such things are cleansed and cleared away when Christ enters a person's heart."

Let us try to understand this whole process of "putting away childish things" and "growing up" from the standpoint of what we commonly call a personality complex.

We used to hear a lot about people who had a certain complex, like an inferiority complex, or a self-punishing complex. We don't use the word as much nowadays, but I believe if we properly understand its meaning it can be helpful.

One definition of *complex* is "a group of repressed desires and memories that exerts a dominating influence upon the personality." In relationship to a harmful childhood motto, we could describe a complex as an unhealthy emotional push from our past. You see, from the time we are born, we are faced with the problem of filling certain basic God-given needs: needs like food, warmth, security, sex, the need to feel worthwhile, the need to belong, the need to be loved and to give love, and the need to feel there is some purpose to our lives.

As we grow up we gradually learn certain means of meeting these great needs. We might call them emotional mechanisms, or ways of coping and fulfilling our needs. These include every form of activity, both conscious and subconscious, of the body and the mind and the spirit. By the time we have reached a certain age (and no one knows exactly when this is) we have adopted a basic pattern for handling life and finding the fulfillment of our needs. These emotional mechanisms and patterns may be right or wrong, good or bad, healthy or unhealthy, or a mixture of these.

I use the term complex to mean an unhealthy set of mechanisms—a wrong pattern or means of meeting life and its needs. A complex is thus a whole set of desires, responses, feelings, and ideas—a whole set of unhealthy mechanisms which have a strong emotional push. This is where some of those childhood mottos and vows come into the picture. They are, in capsule form, an unhealthy push from the past. Can you understand now why Christian experience does not of itself automatically cure these complexes or reprogram unhealthy childhood mottos?

## PERSONAL REFLECTION

■ What coping mechanisms have you developed over the years to meet your basic God-given needs? In a brief sentence, describe how you are getting each of the following needs met in your life at present.

Your need for food, warmth, and security: _____

_____

_____

Your sexual needs: _____

_____

_____

Your need to feel worthwhile: _____

_____

_____

Your need to belong: _____

_____

_____

Your need to be loved and to give love: _____

_____

_____

Your need for a sense of purpose in life: _____

_____

_____

■ Were any of your God-given needs NOT met in appropriate ways as a child? Which ones? What difference do you think it makes in your life TODAY because those basic needs weren't meet when you were growing up?

_____

_____

_____

_____

_____

Paul Tournier in his great book, *The Person Reborn* (Harper & Row, pp. 6–7), explains it so clearly in a parable. He says that a Christian experience is like a revolution. A new prince has taken over a country by means of a coup détat. Among the crowd that acclaims him are the followers of the fallen monarch who is now powerless. For the moment they seem to be the most zealous partisans of the new ruler. But their change of heart is not sincere, for they are the enemy who will secretly scheme the gradual undermining of the new regime. If the reigning prince wins some triumph they bow down and pretend to submit, only to raise their heads once again at the first opportunity to undermine his power.

Tournier says that this is what happens in the case of some of the deeply submerged elements in our mental makeup. They hide themselves and share in the victory we feel. But they have not capitulated, and they may later succeed in sabotaging those victories if we do not unmask them. The process of unmasking them, he says, is a slow one and may require the help of medicine, psychiatry, and spiritual power.

This is an effective illustration of how a person can be a very genuine Christian and still have certain emotional conflicts and complexes which need the gradual healing and Christianizing work of the Holy Spirit. Imagine my great surprise to find that years ago one of our great theologians, Daniel Steele, used almost this same illustration in saying that a Christian can even experience the deeper aspect of sanctification and yet be plagued by what he calls "infirmities." In his *Milestone Papers* (Phillips and Hunt, p. 208), Steele talks about living in a country called "Perfect Love." He soon discovers:

> There are old residents of this country who are by no means favorites of mine, and I cut their acquaintance as much as possible—such as Ignorance, Forgetfulness, Misjudgment, Error, Inadvertence, Failure, and a large family by the name of Infirmity. In fact, I have repeatedly cast my vote for their exclusion but they insist they have a right to remain. They say they are grossly wronged when confounded with an odious foreigner called Sin, who slightly resembles them, but is wholly different in moral character. Hence, I live in peace with these old citizens, but do not delight in their society!

I realize that these illustrations are not perfect and Steele's statements are oversimplified. However, for most of us they will help. Let us consider our crisis Christian experience as the coup détat, the moment of revolution when the New Prince takes over; and then let us look at the growth in Christlikeness and in emotional maturity as the mopping-up process whereby every part of our personality is brought under the total lordship of our Prince and Lord—Jesus Christ!

## PERSONAL REFLECTION

■ As both Tournier and Steele point out, becoming a Christian does not necessarily guarantee that all of the old "defects of character" which are so much a part of the "old nature," will automatically disappear from our lives when we become Christians. Are there any areas of your life that seem to resist the work of the Holy Spirit and continue to cause you to feel spiritually defeated? What are they? Name the specific character defects/sins with which you struggle.

_____

_____

_____

_____

_____

■ Respond to this statement: "Every part of your personality needs to be brought under the total lordship of Jesus Christ." What does "total lordship" look and feel like to you? Does lordship conjour up positive or negative feelings? Why?

_____

_____

_____

_____

_____

Essentially there are two complexes which result from the unhealthy inner push of the "Measure up" motto:

The inferiority complex which makes us feel inadequate and unable, and fills us with self-depreciation.

The impeccability complex which makes us feel as if we should and could do better than we did and fills us with self-belittling. The impeccability complex is commonly called perfectionism because those who have it somehow feel that they need to do everything perfectly. They must be impeccable in their performance.

It's easy to see why these two are always interconnected, like Siamese twins. Since these people can never quite measure up, they are never satisfied with what they do, and therefore always berate themselves and feel inferior. Since they have been programmed to think that their sense of value and worth depends entirely on measuring up, they do not feel good about themselves. It's a built-in guarantee of low self-esteem and poor self-worth.

**PERSONAL REFLECTION**

■ Do you have an "inferiority complex"? Describe a time when you belittled yourself or backed out of a situation or relationship because you felt inadequate or inferior.

_____

_____

_____

_____

■ Are you a perfectionist? Three favorite phrases of the perfectionist are: "could have," "should have," "would have." Monitor your perfectionistic thinking this week by recording any instances when you catch yourself using one of the phrases just mentioned.

_____

_____

_____

_____

_____

_____

_____

_____

In my book, *Healing for Damaged Emotions* (Victor), I have dealt rather extensively with this in several chapters on healing low self-esteem, perfectionism, and depression. However, let me make a few practical suggestions which can help you break the compulsive power of this unhealthy push from your childhood.

Try to see this for what it really is—not the voice of God, not the voice of conscience (though it may seem to be both), but a lie from your childhood and teenage past. This is where you will have to deal very definitely and decisively with it and *katargeo* it! It will help if you can make a distinction between the healthy pursuit of excellence and the unhealthy striving after standards which are beyond reach, reason, and the Word of God. This will not be easy, but it is essential. And it will require time and effort: "Anyone who lives on milk, being still an infant, is not acquainted with the teaching about righteousness. But solid food is for the mature, who by constant use have trained themselves to distinguish good from evil. Therefore, let us leave the elementary teachings about Christ and go on to maturity, not laying again the foundation of repentance" (Hebrews 5:12–6:1, NIV). Another version renders it, "For those who have their faculties trained by practice to distinguish good from evil" (5:14, RSV). It is plain that God's Word considers this training and practice an essential part of leaving spiritual babyhood and growing up into spiritual adulthood.

You may not be able to do this on your own. You may need to share with a trusted friend or a pastor or Christian counselor who can help you sort out what is really coming from God and His Word, and what is simply your "never-able-to-please" inner child, pushing you toward impossible goals. Sometimes these feelings are so severe as to require a long period of time with a well-trained Christian counselor. But whatever it takes, make up your mind to "render inoperative" this insistent voice of the relentless, clamoring kid inside of you.

## PERSONAL REFLECTION

■ Are you able to distinguish between the healthy pursuit of excellence and perfectionism? Give an example of pursuing excellence in your life. Then describe something you've done that reveals perfectionism at work in your life.

_____

_____

_____

_____

_____

■ In what ways is perfectionism ruling your life at present? Are you ready to see it for what it really is? Why or why not?

_____

_____

_____

_____

Cooperate with the Holy Spirit in trying to level off the roller coaster mood swings that usually go along with the "Measure up" complex. I have counseled well over a thousand people who have been troubled with this problem and find that most of them have an "all-or-nothing" outlook. Their world has only two colors—black or white. If they don't achieve perfection, then they are total failures. This keeps them on emotional and spiritual highs and lows. They often describe themselves as "spiritual yo-yos"!

I've often wondered whether or not Simon Peter didn't have a touch of this. Have you ever noticed how much of an "all-or-nothing" guy Peter tended to be? On the Mount of Transfiguration he was afraid, yet found it exciting (he wanted to build booths and stay up there forever). At the Last Supper he said to Jesus, "Lord, You're not going to wash my feet. I can't let You do a thing like that!" Then when Jesus rebuked him, notice Peter's response: "OK, Lord, wash not only my feet, but my head and my hands." He swung from "Not even my feet!" to "Give me a bath!"

In those last hours, Jesus said that someone was going to betray Him. Peter declared, "Lord, I don't know about anyone else. They might do it, but though everybody else in the whole world would deny You, I'll die for You!" Within a few hours when a maid kidded Peter a little, he scoffed, "Who? Jesus? Why, I've never even heard of the man. Who's he?"

Aren't you glad that Jesus Himself said to someone like Peter, "Simon, Simon, behold Satan has desired to have you that he may sift you as wheat. But I have prayed for you that your faith may not fail, and when you have turned again, strengthen your brethren" (Luke 22:31-32, RSV). And in the same patient way, Jesus Himself has prayed for you too (John 17:20) and is even now interceding for you (Hebrews 7:25). Through His Spirit He is here to help you, even as He helped Peter through his many mood swings and spiritual ups and downs. And, just as He finally was able to get Peter leveled off so that the unpredictable and unstable Simon became Cephas, a rocklike apostle, so He will do the same for you. Peter learned how to become stabilized and steady and has told us how to do it: "Grow in grace and knowledge of our Lord and Savior Jesus Christ" (2 Peter 3:18).

**PERSONAL REFLECTION**

■ People who are not emotionally grown-up tend to operate in extremes, as evidenced in the life of Simon Peter. Do you ever think or act in extreme ways? This week, keep track of situations where you find yourself reacting in "all-or-nothing," "black-and-white" kinds of ways. Record those situations. Then reread what you've written at the end of the week.

_____

_____

_____

_____

_____

_____

_____

_____

■ Second Peter 3:18 provides hope for those who want to become emotionally and spiritually mature Christians—"Grow in grace and knowledge of our Lord and Savior Jesus Christ." Describe what you think it means "to grow in grace" as it relates to knowing Jesus Christ. How much of God's grace do you know at a heartfelt level?

_____

_____

_____

_____

_____

That's how it came about with Roger and Barb—a couple who came to me for help in the midst of their stormy marriage. In spite of regular "family devotions" and a deep commitment to Christ and their church, they found their marriage coming apart at the seams. They were all the more dejected and defeated because they were genuine believers and had tried so hard to put the Lord into their relationship—from courtship right on through several years of married life. A time of private counseling with each of them revealed that they were both victims of the "Measure up" treatment. He was from a solid Christian home and she from a totally secular one, but the basic atmospheres had been almost identical. Any kind of outstanding performance on either of their parts had been rewarded with approval. But when either one failed to do "their best" or made even the smallest mistake, their parents had reacted with disappointment and took it as a "poor reflection" on themselves, saying, "I wonder what they think of your mother and father; they must think we're terrible parents." This scene was a common occurrence in both Roger's and Barb's families. And because their parents' security and self-esteem was made to hinge on Roger's and Barb's successful performances, a "guilt trip" was laid on them. So "Measure up"—meaning—"Look what you're doing to our reputation when you fail," was built right into their personalities. Can you imagine what this kind of an outlook would do to the many difficult adjustments of the first years of marriage? Well, you're right; it did!

However, once they understood what was really happening between them, they were able to share their hurts and needs with one another on a deep level. Praying together in specific terms enabled Roger and Barb to put away their childish attitudes and not to expect the kind of perfection from each other that is found only in God. It was amazing how much growth they were able to telescope into a few months. Now they rejoice that God brought them together so they could break the vicious cycle that had been operating in both families for several generations. When their first child was born they talked with me about "the joy of starting a whole new tribe" which would come to understand the unconditional love of God through their relationship!

A.W. Tozer's prayer, which precedes a chapter on the love of God (*The Knowledge of the Holy*, Harper, p. 104), is a fitting way to close this chapter.

Our Father which are in heaven, we Thy children are often troubled in mind, hearing within us at once the affirmations of faith and the accusations of conscience. We are sure that there is in us nothing that could attract the love of One as holy and as just as Thou art. Yet Thou hast declared Thine unchanging love for us in Christ Jesus. If nothing in us can win Thy love, nothing in the universe can prevent Thee from loving us. Thy love is uncaused and undeserved. Thou art Thyself the reason for the love wherewith we are loved. Help us to believe the intensity, the eternity of the love that has found us. Then love will cast out fear; and our troubled hearts will be at peace, trusting not in what we are but in what Thou hast declared Thyself to be. Amen.

## PRAYERFUL REFLECTION

■ You can neither do anything SO BAD, nor anything SO GOOD to deserve more or less of God's love and grace. He gives both freely—unconditionally. Complete the following prayer, putting into words how you feel about no longer having to "Measure up" in order to be loved or approved of by God.

*Lord Jesus,*

*Knowing You love and approve of me* _____

_____

_____

_____

_____

_____

_____

_____

## PERSONAL RENEWAL

■ Paul, in his letter to the Romans, reassures us that, in Christ, we are unconditionally loved and accepted by God—forever! Try to grasp the full meaning of this spiritual truth as you reflect on Romans 8:1, 38-39 (NASB) this week.

*There is therefore now no condemnation for those who are in Christ Jesus. . . . For I am convinced that neither death, nor life, nor angels, nor principalities, nor things present, nor things to come, nor powers,*

*nor height, nor depth, nor any other created thing,*
*shall be able to separate us from the love of God,*
*which is in Christ Jesus our Lord.*

*And He entered again into a synagogue; and a man was there with a withered hand. And they were watching him to see if He would heal him on the Sabbath, in order that they might accuse Him. And He said to the man with the withered hand, "Rise and come forward!" And He said to them, "Is it lawful on the Sabbath to do good or to do harm, to save life, or to kill?" But they kept silent. And after looking around at them with anger, grieved at their hardness of heart, He said to the man, "Stretch out your hand." And he stretched it out, and his hand was restored.*

*Mark 3:1-5*

*Jesus wept.*

*John 11:35*

*And He took with Him Peter and James and John, and began to be very distressed and troubled. And He said to them, "My soul is deeply grieved to the point of death; remain here and keep watch." And He went a little beyond them and fell to the ground, and began praying that if it were possible, the hour might pass Him by.*

*Mark 14:33-35*

# Chapter 4
# Another Childhood Motto

Another harmful childhood motto comes out of our misdirected culture: "Brave boys don't cry." This one has impaired many a man and wrecked millions of marriages. It can also be the subtle controlling force in a woman's life. This motto takes several forms—unhelpful sayings such as, "Children are to be seen and not heard," or, "If you don't stop crying, I'll give you something to cry about!" And our cultural overemphasis on certain sports, the adulation of the "strong, silent person," and the inference that if one expresses his emotions he is weak—all these add strength to this destructive motto. Among Christians there are many who give the impression that it is wrong to express any other emotion than "Praise the Lord!"

Some of us had this deadly childhood motto so woven into our lives that as adults we are simply not able to express our real feelings. If feelings do surface, we don't know how to handle them. We feel ashamed or afraid or dirty or weak. We think we are a very poor Christian for even having the emotions, whether we express them or not. So the translation of this childhood script in an adult Christian is, "Good Christians don't express their true feelings," or, Good Christians must never express any negative feelings."

<table>
<tr><td>

**PERSONAL
REFLECTION**

</td><td>

■ Which of the following statements do you remember hearing or sensing in your family as a child? Check all with which you identify.

_____ "Brave boys don't cry."

_____ "If you don't stop crying, I'll give you something to cry about."

</td></tr>
</table>

69

_____ "Crying is a sign of weakness."
_____ "Tears are manipulative."
_____ "Children are to be seen and not heard."
_____ "Parents are always right."
_____ "You must always be strong—especially when other people are watching."
_____ "Anger is bad . . . never express your anger."
_____ "Good Christians never express negative feelings."

■ Are there any other mottos you learned to live by in your family which are not listed above? In the space provided below, list other childhood mottos that come to mind.

_____

_____

_____

_____

_____

_____

■ To what degree do these childhood mottos continue to influence your life today? Name specific ways in which you find yourself still living out these mottos in your life.

_____

_____

_____

_____

_____

_____

_____

Rather than go into any deep discussion of emotions from the standpoint of health and psychology, I believe it will be best to counter this destructive motto by looking at the One who is not only the pioneer and perfecter of our faith, but our example in all things—our Lord Jesus Himself. So let us consider the emotional life of Jesus and see what part feelings played in His life and just exactly how He handled them.

I am so glad that Jesus was literally one of us. In fact, He was far more human in regard to His emotions than many evangelical Christians. For many of us have been badly misled by the combination of a Puritan and more recent macho tradition which has been very destructive, particularly to men. We feel it may be all right for a woman to express her emotions, but not a man—a real Christian he-man. He must not reveal his feelings. Many boys and some girls are trained this way.

And the attitude carries over into the Christian life. To be a really victorious Christian means we should always be quiet and calm and unruffled. We should never be grieved or upset, sorrowful or angry, or moved much by anything. We have falsely made a kind of a "great-stone-face," expressionless, highly controlled, unemotional stoicism the prime evidence of being an overcoming Christian.

## PERSONAL REFLECTION

■ Does the concept Dr. Seamands describes in the previous paragraph about what it means to be a "victorious Christian" fit the picture you've come to understand from your church and/or family? Have you felt "victorious" as a Christian? Why or why not?

_____

_____

_____

_____

_____

■ In what ways do you think this concept of Christianity might actually keep you from, rather than lead you toward, experiencing _real_ victory in your walk with God?

_____

_____

_____

_____

■ What aspects of your Christian walk do you feel best about at this moment? Are there any areas where you seem to continually struggle? What are they? Why do you think these areas are particularly difficult for you?

_____

_____

_____

If Jesus is our pattern, then this is a grotesque misrepresentation. It is a distorted image to put before people as an ideal. Because these unscriptural and unrealistic standards are false, they are therefore unreachable. And yet many sincere Christians try to reach them and experience a great deal of unnecessary guilt in the process. That's why "Brave boys don't cry" often follows closely on the heels of "Measure up," producing a vicious circle of striving, failing, despairing, repenting—restriving, refailing, and redespairing in which so many Christians live.

Jesus was never afraid to express His emotions, never ashamed to let people see and know how He really felt. So let's look at some of life's deepest and most important emotions and see just how Jesus handled them.

A few years ago some English archeologists, digging in the sands of Egypt, found a tomb inside a cave which had been sealed for almost 4,000 years. They broke through the outer coverings and came on a beautiful carved stone coffin; on the outside was the name of a little girl. Centuries ago, two heartbroken parents had laid to rest their only daughter. As the archeologists were about to open the sarcophagus, they discovered another inscription. It said, "O my life, my love, my little one, would God I had died for Thee!" The two men looked at each other and shook their heads, and once again sealed the cave. They were so moved by what they saw they just couldn't bear to intrude into the privacy of those sorrowing parents. They left love and death to their eternal vigil.

We can understand their reactions as they were confronted by something more important than archeological research. They were moved by a sorrow 4,000 years old. Grief over the death of someone you love is one of life's strongest emotions.

## PERSONAL REFLECTION

■ Every one of us at one time or another loses someone or something that is very important to us. Grief is the natural unavoidable emotional reaction to loss. Looking back at our losses and how they affected us is very painful, but it is inevitably more painful if we don't. Listed below are some of the losses you may have experienced in your life up to this point. Spend a little extra time journaling your responses to only those questions below which relate to your specific losses. *NOTE: Additional space for journaling is provided in the back of this workbook.*

**Loss through Death:** List any important people in your life who have died. What was your relationship to each person? How old were you when each person died? What needs was each person meeting which are no longer being met?

_____

_____

_____

_____

_____

**Loss through Divorce:** Have you been through a divorce either as a child or as an adult? How did the divorce change your life? Are there issues today regarding the divorce that you still need to address?

_____

_____

_____

_____

_____

_____

**Loss of a Boyfriend or Girlfriend:** Is there anyone from the past that you have had a hard time letting go of emotionally? Name any previous "loves" and describe the relationship you shared with each. What caused your relationship to end? Do you still think about him or her? What do you miss that was part of that love relationship?

_____

_____

_____

_____

_____

**Loss of a Home:** Have you lost a home to a fire, flood, earthquake, or any other natural disaster? Or has a foreclosure or bankruptcy robbed you of your home? Describe the circumstances surrounding your loss. How did the loss of your home effect you emotionally? Spiritually? Relationally?

_____

_____

_____

_____

_____

_____

**Loss of a Job:** Have you ever been fired or layed-off from a job? What were the circumstances surrounding your job loss? How long did you remain unemployed after you lost your job? What emotions related to your job loss do you remember feeling?

_____

_____

_____

_____

_____

**Loss Due to an Illness or Accident:** Have you, or has any member of your family had a major physical trauma or loss? How did the loss affect your role in the family? Did you grieve your loss? Why or why not?

_____

_____

_____

_____

_____

**Loss of a Dream:** Have you experienced the loss of a dream related to marriage? Having children? Achieving a certain job status, position, or salary level? Make a list of the hopes and dreams you've had for your life. What disappointments, related to those dreams, have you experienced?

_____

_____

_____

_____

_____

_____

What should be our reaction to this universal human experience? How did Jesus handle grief and sorrow?

There are two great incidents which give us a clue. The first is Jesus' reaction when they brought Him the news that John the Baptist, His own cousin whom He admired so deeply, had been beheaded. "Now when Jesus heard it, He withdrew from there in a boat to a lonely place by Himself" (Matthew 14:13). Isn't that what we all feel like doing when the bad news first comes? We want to get away from people and be by ourselves.

It's not necessarily self-pity or escapism. It is the natural way we first respond to sorrow. Sometime later, Jesus called His disciples and took them apart from the crowds to be by themselves. After that He left them and went by Himself to pray (vv. 22-23).

Here is a beautiful pattern we can all follow: withdrawal for a while, but not for too long. For if you grieve too long by yourself you may lose your sense of balance and perspective. You may turn in on yourself and then find you are grieving not over someone you have lost, but for yourself. So the next thing to do is to get with your closest friends. And certainly to pray, to spend time with your closest friend, the great Comforter.

Although Jesus took time to spend with His friends, and then to withdraw for hours of prayer, He never for a moment forgot the needs of others. He helped them, fed them. For Jesus there was the great healing therapy which comes from work and from doing something for someone else, even in the midst of sorrow.

■ What is your first response to grief? Describe a time when you grieved because of a loss in your life.

_____

_____

_____

_____

_____

_____

■ In her book, _Death and Dying,_ Dr. Elisabeth Kubler-Ross brought world attention to the grief process. She suggested that there are five stages of grief:

Stage 1 - **Denial** - "This can't really be happening to me."
Stage 2 - **Anger** - "Why me?"
Stage 3 - **Bargaining** - "God, if only You will not _____ _____, then I will _____."
Stage 4 - **Sadness** - "I hurt and feel very sad."
Stage 5 - **Acceptance** - " I did experience a loss, but my life will go on."

There is no dictated amount of time one must grieve to finally come to the end of a loss. Nor is there an exact sequence one must go through to get through the five stages of grief. Each loss in life and each person who grieves is unique. There is, perhaps, only one rule of thumb when it comes to grief: the greater the loss, the greater the amount of time it will take to work through the grief process.

■ Have you ever been told by well-meaning family members or friends that you needed to "quit grieving" and move on with your life? Describe what you felt when they suggested you deal with your grief within their time frame?

_____

_____

_____

_____

_____

■ How easy is it for you to reach out to other people when you are grieving? How about to God—are you able to freely go to Him for comfort? Why or why not?

_____

_____

_____

_____

The second incident portrays Jesus at the tomb of Lazarus. From this we see two more insights into how Jesus handled sorrow. "Jesus wept" (John 11:35). Thank God for that great little verse. It's not there just to help Sunday School kids who need a quick verse to recite. It has profound meaning. Jesus cried and He wasn't the least bit ashamed to admit His sorrow and to express it openly. He must have wept very freely because the following verse says that the bystanders commented, "Behold how He loved him!" But the next thing He did was to pray. And He kept reminding the mourners about the resurrection.

These are proper ways to handle grief. They are natural and normal, human and helpful. You never need be ashamed of weeping or withdrawing for a time, or getting help from your closest friends, or praying, or talking about heaven and the Resurrection. This is the right way, the Christian way, to handle sorrow. And one that is good to keep in mind, for you never know when you may be struck by grief, perhaps the commonest of all human emotions. When that voice from your past scolds you with "Brave boys don't cry," talk back to it and say, "That's a lie. Jesus, the bravest of them all, cried!"

## PERSONAL REFLECTION

■ Read the account of Jesus grieving for His friend Lazarus in John 11:17-36. As you read, jot down all the feelings Jesus or other main characters in the passage expressed, whether directly or through inference.

_____

_____

_____

_____

_____

■ What do you learn from this passage about expressing your feelings?

_____

_____

_____

_____

_____

A more difficult emotion to deal with is anger—the most taboo emotion of all among Christians. Did Jesus ever show anger? As He was about to heal the man with the withered hand on the Sabbath, "He looked around at them with anger, grieved at their hardness of heart" (Mark 3:5, RSV). This is the only place in the New Testament which actually uses the word *angry* to describe Jesus. Even when He drove out the money changers, it doesn't say so, though we can assume that He was angry. But this case must have been so evident — without any attempt on the part of Jesus to keep the anger out of His face or to cover the angry tone in His voice—that it is specifically recorded. There must not have been any word other than anger to express His emotion.

Bertand Russell in his famous pamphlet, "Why I Am Not a Christian," uses this incident as proof that Jesus was not perfect as His followers claimed Him to be. Russell claims that Jesus got angry and lost His temper, thus showing His imperfectness. There are a lot of us who, though we may not have said it so blatantly, may wonder about this story or the one about driving the money changers out of the temple.

I believe that Christ's anger was part of His very perfection which was never more accurately expressed than in these moments of white-hot anger. For to say that Christ never got angry would not be to say that He was perfect. It would not be the greatest compliment. Rather, it would be the height of imperfection, for it would demonstrate a great flaw in His divine character. For the Bible speaks often of the anger of God—365 times, in fact. This anger is not an outburst of childish rage. In His anger, Jesus did not slip out of character.

It's high time some of us get over our childish ideas on this subject. Anger is not a sinful emotion. In fact, there are no sinful emotions. There are only sinful uses of emotions. And there are many of us who misuse our emotion of anger, just as the blundering musician can misuse both instrument and music, taking notes intended for beautiful harmony and battering them into senseless discord. Anger is a divinely implanted emotion. Closely allied to our instinct for right, it is designed—as are all our emotions—to be used for constructive spiritual purposes.

The person who cannot feel anger at evil is a person who lacks enthusiasm for good. If you cannot hate the wrong, it's very questionable whether you really love righteousness.

Anger is not weakness; rather, it is great strength. The Bible nowhere condemns anger as a feeling. It does condemn the wrong quality of anger and warns us against inviting, nurturing, or holding on to that kind. And it plainly condemns many wrong actions which are likely to follow such angry feelings.

However, anger which fulfills the same conditions that Jesus' anger did, is the right kind. Such anger must be directed at something that is obviously wrong and evil. It must be controlled, well in hand, and under the direction of the will—not simply a heated passion out of control. And perhaps most important of all, there must not be in it any malice, bitterness, resentment, or hate.

## PERSONAL REFLECTION

■ Anger can be expressed in many different ways. Which of the following seem to be the most common forms your anger takes? Check all that apply.

_____ I express impatience.
_____ I use sarcasm.
_____ I feel and express frustration.
_____ I withdraw emotionally and sometimes physically.
_____ I become obsessive in my thinking.
_____ I avoid the person I am angry with.
_____ My tone of voice becomes authoritative.
_____ I hold grudges.
_____ I become more aggressive than usual.
_____ I give the person I'm angry with the "silent treatment."
_____ I retaliate by slandering or gossiping about the person I'm angry with.
_____ I take on an "I-don't-care" attitude.
_____ I am kind on the outside but feel totally unkind on the inside.
_____ I get depressed.

■ Make a list of four situations in your life that have caused you to feel angry. How was your anger expressed in each situation?

_____

_____

_____

_____

_____

_____

_____

■ What messages about anger were communicated to you as a child? A teenager? As a maturing adult?

_____

_____

_____

_____

_____

■ Do you agree or disagree with Dr. Seamands' statement: "Anger is not weakness; rather, it is great strength"? Explain why you feel the way you do.

_____

_____

_____

_____

_____

■ _Optional Art Exercise:_ Draw a picture or do a collage of your anger. This anger is to be from your past and present experiences. _NOTE: Use a page of the Supplemental Journaling Pages section in Appendix Three to complete this art project._

In Mark 3 we see Jesus on the Sabbath being confronted by a man with a withered hand—a man in great need. Scores of people are watching Him. Do they hope to see Him heal this poor man and enable him to be a useful worker once more? No. They have no eye for a miracle. They're watching to see if He'll break one of their laws. They would rather see a man with a useless hand stay that way—helpless and unable to work for a living—than to see one of their religious rules broken. They were not only blind but cruel.

No wonder Jesus got angry. But look a little more closely at the verse. "He looked around at them with anger, grieved at their hardness of heart" (Mark 3:5, RSV). Note how carefully Jesus' anger fulfilled the right conditions. It was for an unselfish and a completely righteous cause: a man's livelihood and health were at stake. His anger was controlled. There was no outburst, no paroxysm. No one could say, "Jesus got so mad that He couldn't see straight!" He was the only One who was seeing straight. The people were so hardened that they had become blind and deaf—oblivious to the great need of this man.

The late Charles Jefferson once said, "So prone is anger to mix itself with base and unlovely elements, so frequently does it stir up the mud at the bottom of the soul that it is not easy to free our minds from the feeling that anger has something sinful in it: or . . . that it is an unlovely flaw in conduct, a deformity of character from which we pray to be delivered" (*The Character of Jesus*, Crowell, p.116).

But here we see it, not stirred up by any muddy depths of passion, but flowing white-hot anger, out of true holiness and loving concern for people.

## PERSONAL REFLECTION

■ Some might call the type of anger Jesus expressed in Mark 3, "righteous indignation." Can you recall a time when you witnessed something being done to someone that was abusive or unfair? Describe the situation and the feelings you remember having about what was happening at the time.

_____

_____

_____

_____

_____

■ Overall, how would you rate yourself in terms of your "loving concern" for people (i.e., what is your empathy and compassion quotient)?

_____

Above all, mark the words *anger* and *grieved*, for there's the real picture. Here are two great emotions which we often think are opposites, not to be mixed any more than fire and water. But in His heart they were. There was no malice, no resentment, just great grief and compassion and love. Anger, which fell on the evil they did, and sorrow for those who did it. Anger and compassion are opposite sides of the same coin.

Did you ever stop to consider that maybe the reason your love for Christ is so lukewarm, or even cold, is because you do not get angry enough, do not hate evil enough?

Did you ever stop to consider how much good has been accomplished in the world when good people finally got angry enough at wrong to do something about it?

Martin Luther said, "When I am angry, I preach well and pray better." Dr. William Channing said, "Ordinarily, I weigh 120 pounds, but when I'm mad, I weigh a ton!" The history of reform is replete with illustrations.

English prisoners used to be kept in vile, disease-ridden prisons that were described as a veritable hell-on-earth. But John Howard and his followers got angry and did something about it.

Slavery was a deeply entrenched evil in this New World until men like William Lloyd Garrison "saw in the sorrowful face of the slave the shadowed face of God." Nerved by a righteous anger that would not be silenced, Garrison shouted, "I will not retreat a single inch. And I will be heard!"

Young Abe Lincoln, watching a slave market for the first time, got sick to his stomach and a passionate white-hot anger rose in him. His fingernails bit into his hands and he whispered so fiercely that everyone heard him, "That's wrong, and if I ever get a chance to hit it, I'll hit it hard!"

Milan hospitals were horrible until Florence Nightingale came along. One of her biographers presents her not as a gentle angel of mercy, but as a stubborn, angry woman with a clear call from God to unrelentingly pursue government officials until they provided humane treatment for the wounded and the dying. Those officials shuddered at the mention of her name.

Anger is not necessarily the opposite of love. Sometimes it is the result of love and its clearest expression. Never pray for your anger to be removed or taken away from you. That's as mistaken and immature as asking God to remove all sexual desires from your life.

Pray rather that your temper be cleansed and brought under the Spirit's control. Pray not that anger be eradicated, but that it be redirected to that which makes God angry.

PERSONAL
REFLECTION

■ Are you able to express your anger in a mature and balanced way? If not, why not? If yes, explain how you learned to find the appropriate balance.

_____

_____

_____

_____

_____

Finally, what shall we call this emotion of our Lord's struggle in the Garden? A troubled spirit, in the sense of trying to find and do God's clear will for His life. His struggle is difficult to describe because it was a complex combination of several emotions.

There was loneliness in it. Jesus asked His inner circle—Peter, James, and John—to stand by Him and pray for Him. "My soul is deeply grieved even to the point of death; remain here and keep watch" (Mark 14:34). Later on, "Could you not keep watch for one hour?" (v. 37) When He so desperately needed the prayers and support of His inner circle of friends, they failed Him. He was alone and hurting from loneliness.

There was the struggle of temptation in it. Before He asked the three to go with Him, He told them they were the ones who had stood by Him in His temptations (Luke 22:28). Jesus' temptations didn't end with the wilderness tempting, early in His ministry. The devil left Him for a season, but he came back , and often. He was back now trying to use Jesus' anguish of spirit, His despair and depression, to cause Him to turn from the Father's will and seek His own. We cannot say exactly what emotions Christ was experiencing. They were so powerful as to cause physical effects: profuse sweating—as it were, drops of blood; and trembling—even falling on the ground.

Why am I going into detail here? Because of an idea many of us have. We think if we have a great spiritual struggle, if we are racked and shaken by severe conflict and temptation, if we don't easily and automatically find and affirm God's will, there is something wrong with us. We are not truly Spirit-filled.

This is a caricature of the truth. Victory is not automatic, and will usually involve a struggle within our emotions. And we should not be ashamed or try to hide it, for our Lord didn't.

We all go through Gethsemanes—our times of struggle when we, like Jesus, have to pray, "Father, You know my deepest feelings, what my emotions want. But Your will, not mine, be done!"

## PERSONAL REFLECTION

■ What situations have caused you to "agonize" over knowing and doing God's will in your life?

_____

_____

_____

_____

_____

■ In what ways have loneliness and temptation proved to be spiritual obstacles in knowing and doing the will of God in your life?

_____

_____

_____

_____

_____

We have looked in considerable detail at the way Jesus experienced and expressed His emotions. As the perfect human, Jesus understood a principle which psychologists have only recently discovered! Any experience for which you do not make the required payment of emotion, you will later pay for with compounded interest. Jesus responded to each experience with the appropriate emotional expression. Therefore, we never find Him suffering from what we now call a "delayed reaction." Jesus did not believe that "brave boys don't cry." Let us nail that fantasy for what it is—a lie from our childhood or teenage days. Let us be done with it, freeing ourselves from its emotional imprisonment. And then, let us grow up in Christlikeness—free to experience our emotions and to let others know what we feel.

In this way we shall become truly mature. For maturity is both wholeness and holiness. Mature holiness means recovering our true humanness. At the heart of holiness and wholeness is knowing and loving God and other people, including ourselves. The sanctifying process is essentially a humanizing process. The holier you become the more human you become, because you become more like Jesus, the only perfect human being who has ever lived. He possessed perfect sanctity, perfect sanity, perfect deity, and perfect humanity.

Unfortunately, a lot of our training from childhood mottos has programmed us to look at holiness in a dehumanizing way. As a result Christian piety and holiness often take the form of withdrawal from the enjoyment of God's creation. Our lives become rigid, starved of genuine, free-flowing love, and devoid of human warmth. But we don't have to live that way. If our emotional systems have been wrongly programmed by unchristian data, they can be reprogrammed by the Holy Spirit. Instead of being God's frozen people, we can become His holy and wholesome children.

## PERSONAL REFLECTION

■ Have Christian friends ever used 2 Corinthians 5:17 (TLB)—*When someone becomes a Christian, he becomes a brand new person inside. He is not the same anymore. A new life has begun!*—or Philippians 3:13b (TLB)—*. . . Forgetting the past and looking forward to what lies ahead, . . . .* to try to convince you that you don't need to deal with emotionally damaging situations and feelings from the past? How do you reconcile what these verses seem to be saying with Dr. Seamands' statement, "Any experience for which you do not make the required payment of emotion, you will pay for with compounded interest." What do you think the "required payment" for damaged emotions is?

_____

_____

_____

_____

_____

_____

## PRAYERFUL REFLECTION

■ Dr. Seamands states, "Mature holiness means recovering our true humanness." This is indeed a profound truth. For the reality is, you will be only as spiritually mature as you are emotionally whole. How committed are you to your own process of emotional and spiritual recovery? In the form of a prayer of commitment, let God know how you feel about the things you've discovered about yourself as you've worked through the material in this chapter. Ask Him for whatever it is you need to continue on your journey toward wholeness.

*Lord Jesus,*

_____

_____

_____

_____

_____

_____

_____

## PERSONAL RENEWAL

■ This week, embrace the reality of living life fully . . . freely . . . as you read and reflect on these words from John 10:10. *NOTE: the personal pronoun* you *has been added in brackets for emphasis.*

*I came that [you] might have life,*
*and that [you] might have it abundantly.*

*We are no longer to be children, tossed here and there by waves, and carried about by every wind of doctrine, by the trickery of men, by craftiness in deceitful scheming; but speaking the truth in love, we are to grow up in all aspects into Him, who is the head, even Christ, from whom the whole body, being fitted and held together by that which every joint supplies, according to the proper working of each individual part, causes the growth of the body for the building up of itself in love.*

*Ephesians 4:14-16*

# Chapter 5
# Childish Ideas of Love and Marriage

Don't you wish everybody would put away their childish ideas about love and marriage? You know the statistics on American marriages— one out of two is destined for dissolution. Do you realize the United States is responsible for one-half of the reported divorces in the entire world? And there are many fractured and broken marriages in this country that are not yet statistics. Though no legal action has been taken, many spouses are just living apart— nearly two million people who are emotionally and spiritually divorced.

If you add to this number the spouses who are unhappy but still together, you come to the frightening conclusion that the average still-married couple in the United States has much less than a fifty-fifty chance of being reasonably happy in their life together. Evangelical Christians aren't exempt and are being added to the divorce statistics at an alarming rate.

Paul reminds us that growing into real maturity means getting rid of our childish understanding. In marriage nothing is more important than that. Too many people come to courtship and marriage thinking, understanding, and communicating like children. No wonder. The fantasy begins on Mother's or Dad's lap during those evening sessions before bedtime, in the story from the fairy tale book where the handsome young prince marries the beautiful young princess. For teenagers the fantasy continues in front of the television set. The mass media is the sickest and the most demonic factor in all of this, filling us with childish and unrealistic concepts. By the time young people begin to date and move into adulthood, they are still thinking and understanding like children.

PERSONAL
REFLECTION

■ What are some of the "fairy tale" fantasies of love and marriage you've held on to? *EXAMPLES: The person I marry must be physically attractive for me to be happy. Real love is invincible—it can overcome any obstacle. The person I marry will satisfy all my needs.*

_____

_____

_____

_____

_____

_____

In the area of love and marriage, psychologists have a fancy name for what St. Paul calls "childish things"—"romantic infantilism." What a contrast there is between this romantic infantilism—a fantasy-filled, feeling-centered love—and the love spoken of in the Bible. This love between husband and wife is so deep, so strong, so committed and enduring in quality, that it is used to illustrate the love Christ has for His church. It's the difference between *reel* love and *real* love.

"How do you know you are in love with him?" I asked some sweet young college coed.

"Oh," she said, "every time I am around him, I really get shook up!"

I asked, "Oh, you mean like a bowl of Jell-O?"

"Yes! That's it exactly!" she responded.

Now I like Jell-O. It makes a good salad or dessert. But you need a lot of other things on the menu if you are going to have a balanced, well-nourished marriage.

Don't for a moment think I am underestimating the part of marriage that shakes you up and turns you on. The feeling element is a very important ingredient in mature Christian love and marriage. Sexual love, eros, physical attraction—this is God's gift, His idea, His plan. He intended it to be an essential part of a mature marriage. And if eros is not a part of your concept of marriage, you are not fit for marriage. I can't think of anything worse than being married for a lifetime to someone who didn't ring my chimes!

Why is it nowadays that so many people are talking more about eros and sex, but enjoying it less? Why the growing rise in impotence related problems? Because as the song says, we have substituted fantasy for reality, "a paper doll" rather than a "real live girl."

That centerfold in *Playboy* magazine may some day prevent you from being a good lover, when you are faced with actually enfolding a real flesh-and-blood marriage partner. Fantasy may become the substitute for reality. You did notice it's called Play*boy*, not Play*man*, didn't you?

Eros, sacramental in the mind of the Christian, is vital and important. But love based only on eros, on desire alone, cannot be stable. No two people in the world will always be desirable to one another. And sometimes they may even seem undesirable. Because time changes external characteristics, eros must increasingly be based on inner beauty for there to be enduring love in the relationship.

## PERSONAL REFLECTION

■ In what ways have you let the world's concept of love—erotic, romanticized love—influence your thinking?

_____

_____

_____

_____

■ *(Women)* Have you ever used "romance novels" to fill a "love void" in your life? What was the attraction for you? How do you think your use of romance novels has impacted your ability to receive and give real love?

_____

_____

_____

_____

■ *(Men)* Have you used pornographic magazines or movies to satisfy your need for intimacy? How has your use of these materials affected your view of women? Marriage? Your own self-esteem? Your relationship with God? From your experience, what are some of the "lies" about love perpetuated by pornography?

_____

_____

_____

_____

_____

_____

_____

■ What steps can you take in your life to safeguard the truth that enduring love is based on inner beauty more than outer beauty?

_____

_____

_____

_____

_____

"Falling in love" is a childish basis for a Christian marriage. You would think love was a mysterious force from outer space that unexpectedly seized two people and overpowered them, a force beyond rational control. However, if love comes that way, it can also leave that way, as mysteriously as it arrived. Several years ago a television heroine and her TV bridegroom spoke their marriage vows, claiming that they would cherish and care for each other "so long as we both shall love." They changed just one letter, and espoused a totally different philosophy of marriage than that which promises to love "as long as we both shall live."

It is childish to think that my love can be measured by the intensity of my own subjective sensations. This is merely being in love with my feelings of love. It is loving myself through another person, which is the most selfish thing in the world. Who characteristically is in love with his own sensations? With himself? A baby, of course. The modern idea of love is merely romantic infantilism. And infantilism with a gross imbalance on eros turns out to be nothing more than a young child's self-love dressed in grown-up clothes, parading on a Hollywood technicolor stage, trying to make a child's fairy-tale fantasy pass for responsible adult drama.

## PERSONAL REFLECTION

■ Explain what you think "falling in love" is all about.

_____

---

---

---

---

■ Now describe what you think enduring love looks like? Have you experienced this kind of love in your life? If not, why not?

---

---

---

---

---

■ When dreams don't come true we experience great disappointment. What are some of the greatest disappointments you've experienced in relationship to love?

---

---

---

---

In Scripture there is a second great word for love: *philia*. *Philia* is love as friendship, the kind of love that develops a common bond between people who see things in the same way, who share the same points of view, who strive together for the same goals.

The Bible forbids a believer to marry anyone who is not also a truly committed Christian. This warning not to be "bound together with unbelievers" (2 Corinthians 6:14) exists because of the nature of *philia* or friendship love, and the basic unity of outlook and interest it presumes. "Can two walk together unless they be agreed?" (Amos 3:3) They can't! They can't even walk together for very long, let alone love and live together in the most serious, intimate, demanding relationship between two human beings. Thus the minimum requirement of philia love is that you be one in Christ with the person you are dating or courting or preparing to marry. Without this oneness in Christ, there is no possibility of a successful marriage.

However, this does not mean that simply because two people are good Christians they will necessarily have a good marriage. We all know wonderful Christians who should have never married each other. For philia includes much more than spiritual unity. It also takes in many important factors of personality blending which make up the rivets in the bonds of matrimony.

It is foolish to overlook this vital element in our thinking about love and marriage. One childish notion, and part of the demonic delusion that comes from the mass media, goes something like this: "I wouldn't think of marrying him—he's too good a friend of mine." "Why I could never fall in love with her—she is too good a friend." Did you ever hear such rubbish? I can't think of a better basis for marriage than the fact that two people are good friends. Or let's consider the reverse of that: Would you really want to spend a lifetime with someone who was not a real friend? When you are courting, a good question to ask yourselves is this: "Are the two of us the kind of people who could have a lifelong friendship even if there were never any sexual expression between us?" It is a pretty difficult question to ask, but it is an important one.

## PERSONAL REFLECTION

■ What are the qualities of a friendship that you value most in your relationships? List them. Are the qualities you listed a part of your dating, courting, and/or marriage relationship? If not, why not?

_____

_____

_____

_____

_____

■ What makes you and the person you are dating/courting/married to compatible? In what ways, if any, are you incompatible? Do you share common interests, values, and goals in life? Are you compatible in terms of your personalities? Are you able to accept the other person as they are today?

_____

_____

_____

_____

_____

■ Why or why not would you want to marry your "best friend"?

_____

_____

_____

_____

■ Describe your "ideal" marriage partner.

_____

_____

_____

_____

By the time we are adults, we have built a whole set of fantasy preferences for our marriage partner. However, the person best suited for you, the person to whom God may guide you, may be very different, even quite the opposite of your dream guy or your dream gal. And this is where you need to understand the third kind of love which is absolutely necessary for a mature marriage— *agape*.

Agape is the love that comes only from God, the love that is godlike in all its characteristics. It is an other-regarding love, a self-sacrificing love. Agape is grounded not in the emotions but in the will. It is not even based on the commonalities of philia or friendship, but is settled in the commitment of the will. It is the commitment to love, in spite of and regardless of.

What does this kind of love look like? If you want to know, read and reread 1 Corinthians 13. It is a manner of behavior, a commitment to care for and protect, to love and to cherish, to assume responsibility for the welfare of that person. It is covenanted devotion, and it can survive all sorts of changes of mood and circumstances.

## PERSONAL REFLECTION

■ Would you say you have experienced agape love in any of your relationships? In what ways has the person you've been dating/are being courted by/or are married to loved you with an agape love? Spend some time examining your most loving relationships this week in the light of 1 Corinthians 13.

_____

_____

_____

_____

_____

Mature Christian marriage combines:
- *Eros*, desire, sexual attraction,
- *Philia*, genuine friendship, unity of interests and purpose,
- *Agape*, deeply covenanted, committed devotion.

Married love is a very precious and precarious balance of all three. Romantic or eros love is a wonderful help in getting a marriage started. It is like the rocket that puts the space capsule into orbit and then drops away. It takes other forms of power to continue that space capsule in its successful flight toward its goal. It takes a putting away of childishly imbalanced concepts of love to have a successful marriage.

"I understood as a child," says Paul, "when I was a child." Yes, but marriage is an adult business. Rather than "falling in love," it might be more accurate from a Christian standpoint to speak of "climbing up into love."

Perhaps the greatest problem in marriage is communication. Paul said, "When I was a child, I spoke like a child, I communicated on a childish level, but now that I have grown up, I am communicating on a mature level." Fortunately for us, Paul defined what he meant by mature communication: "So that we may no longer be children, tossed to and fro . . . rather, speaking the truth in love, we are to grow up in every way" (Ephesians 4:14-15, RSV). How beautiful and how accurate! Paul was two thousand years ahead of his time when it came to basic communication principles. "Speaking the truth in love" is mature Christian communication.

PERSONAL
REFLECTION

■ Give an example of a time when someone spoke the truth to you in an *unloving* way. Then describe an instance when a person's kind and loving words got a hard-hitting truth through to your desensitized heart.

_____

_____

_____

_____

_____

The greatest cause of unhappiness in marriage is the inability of spouses to communicate openly and lovingly with one another. All too often, marital communication is still on a childish level.

How do children communicate? Some children speak the truth all right, but they are cruel, sharp, and hurtful. "Sticks and stones may break my bones, but words will never hurt me." Not true. Harsh words can hurt even the bones, and badly. Children are very cruel at times: they speak the truth, but not in love.

Then there are children who cannot speak the truth. I don't mean that they lie. Rather, they are too afraid of their feelings to express them. It may be that every time they try to express their feelings, they get shut down. Or perhaps they have never seen or heard a true expression of feelings from the people they live with. They may be loving children, but they can't speak the truth.

"Speaking the truth in love" is the secret. That is what makes a strong and mature Christian marriage. But speaking this way is a learned art. Maybe I ought to say it is an unlearned art, because often we first have to unlearn things that our homes and life experiences and our sick culture have taught us. We have to *katargeo* them. Sometimes in agony and sweat and tears and maybe even a little blood, we have to put them off and change our whole way of communicating.

PERSONAL
REFLECTION

■ One essential guideline for effective communication in all relationships is: Say what you think and feel using direct but loving "I" statements. *EXAMPLES: (The right way) "Jerry, I really feel shut out of your world when you read the newspaper at the breakfast table. (The wrong way)* "*It really gets me that you always read the newspaper at the breakfast table.*" Why is the second example the wrong way of communicating thoughts and feelings? Think of two or three statements you have made to your spouse or a significant other that seemed to push the two of you apart rather than draw you together.

_____

_____

_____

_____

_____

_____

■ What is your greatest communication challenge in relationship to your spouse/significant other?

_____

_____

_____

_____

■ How easily are you able to express what you think and feel in your relationships? If you struggle to say what you think and feel, why do you think you struggle?

_____

_____

_____

_____

Isn't it incredible that a married couple can love each other, live together, make love to one another, bring up children together, yet never really communicate to one another what they are actually feeling? And we pastors have contributed to the difficulty. For we have given our parishioners the impression that expressed conflict in marriage is a sin. What this notion fails to take into account is that a husband and a wife are always communicating with each other, in one way or another. And so by failing to say what is really wrong, they express in other unsanctified ways their displeasure, their disagreement, and their anger.

Some people need to unlearn the childish unrealities they may have been taught in the name of Jesus. They need to learn that in the Christian life there is such a thing as constructive conflict, which is the grown-up way to deal with disagreements. For such people keep conflict on a childish, hurtful level. They clam up in silence, thinking they are being patient, good Christians. They walk away from any disagreement because they have been taught that this is spiritual. I often tell the couples I counsel that their basic problem is they never learned to fight like Christians! Much of what passes for "submission" is really a lack of caring enough to confront one another.

Gibson Winter reminds us that conflict is always the price of deepening intimacy between persons and can only be resolved by proper communication. Bad communication comes either from not speaking the truth or from not speaking in love. Either you do a slow burn until you are so filled with anger and resentment that all of a sudden it comes out in hurtful torrents. Or you fake your true feelings and the hurt comes out in other ways.

"When I grew up," said Paul, "I put away childish ways of communicating; I learned to speak the truth in love." That will mean confrontation and conflict, which is ultimately creative and helpful. It will result in resolving the conflict and thus deepening your love.

Helen and I are deeply involved in marriage enrichment seminars. Our favorite communication story is about a couple who attended one such weekend. Debbie wanted to serve supper by candlelight two or three times a week. And Bob would say, "I like to see what I'm eating!" or "Are you trying to poison me?" This little conflict grew until it became a big one.

Every time Debbie used candles, Bob let her know that he just didn't like it. "Candlelight again? . . . Well, I just don't like that . . . But go on, have your candles!" Of course, that ruined the meal and left Debbie hurting. They never talked about it. It was candlelight versus noncandlelight.

Then during one of the communication exercises at the conference, Debbie opened up. She had been a foster child, and the people who finally raised her were very poor. They ate in the kitchen on a bare table. The only light in the room was one light bulb without a shade. It just hung there and swung back and forth every time the kitchen door opened. As a teenager, Debbie had vowed to herself, "When I get married I'm going to have a beautiful house with a separate dining room, and we are going to eat by soft light."

When Debbie finished telling Bob her story, he was so deeply touched that he said, "Oh, Honey, you can have all the candles you want! I understand now." Interestingly enough, when Bob expressed that he understood about the candles, it turned out that Debbie didn't need to have them so often anymore. That is usually the case! All we really want is for someone we love to understand where we're coming from.

## PERSONAL REFLECTION

■ How did your parents resolve their conflicts? Describe what you learned from them about conflict resolution.

_____

_____

_____

_____

_____

■ Explain why you agree or disagree with this statement: "Conflict is always the price of deepening intimacy between persons and can only be resolved by proper communication."

_____

_____

_____

_____

_____

■ How do you respond when you feel that something you've said has been misunderstood?

_____

_____

_____

Don't worry if it seems at first that you are learning to express only your more negative feelings. For as those feelings begin to flow, you will learn to express your deep, positive ones too. It took me years and a lot of agonizing hard work to discover this. In spite of my gift of gab, public speaking ability, and even my honest, open sharing as a counselor, way down deep I am really a loner. When I was eleven years old, my missionary parents brought my brother and me home on furlough. The next year Mother and Dad went back to India, leaving us with our grandmother. We thought we would see Mother and Dad in a few years, but along came World War II and they got stuck in India. The next time I saw my parents was on my twentieth birthday.

I know what it is like to be the only student in the dorm during a special vacation. It can be lonely. At that time I didn't realize that layers of unexpressed feelings were being buried. Not until I married did I discover what I was really like: a lonely, frightened little boy, who could not express his deepest feelings. Oh, yes, I could in sermons—maybe that is God's way of using our infirmities to compensate—and I could listen sensitively when I counseled others. But I couldn't express my feelings to the one person I wanted to more than any other, my wife.

In the early days of our marriage, I so often remember saying to myself, "Tonight is going to be different. This evening when I get home, I am going to tell Helen that I love her." I would rehearse all day long what I was going to say when I got home.

When we went to India as missionaries, I would go out in my jeep to the villages and be gone for weeks at a time. Then I would really rehearse! I'd tell myself, "This time it's going to be different. When I get home I'll take her in my arms and say, 'Honey, I love you.'" But the minute I got to the door, I froze. That old childhood wall came between us. I tried to batter my way through it until my hands were bleeding and torn. It hurt our marriage and both of us despaired.

What needed to happen is that I had to share my deepest self with Helen. What self? That frightened, lonely little boy with all of his weaknesses. I'd been scared to do that all of my life. Oh, I had such a brave front. Helen could express her feelings; she told me her fears and how people got her down. But not me! I was always brave. When Helen expressed inadequacy, I interpreted it as feminine weakness. And I was afraid that if I ever told her how I really felt, we would both dissolve and go down the drain together! I was so bold. "Oh, don't let that get you down," I'd say to her, while all the time inside was this scared, lonely little boy.

But God is faithful. One day the dam broke and I shared my real self, the terrified, lonely kid inside of me. I told her everything, at times sobbing uncontrollably. And you know, the most wonderful thing happened! I found out that she wasn't weak—she was amazingly strong. She opened like a flower to the sun. She sustained me and gave me strength. And best of all, when my false front cracked and she saw what I was really like, I discovered that I could express my love freely. The log jam was broken and the stream could flow freely. I could express my deepest feelings, both positive and negative.

Christians with conflicts? Yes, God's people are to be creative and mature. No longer are they to be children tossed about by feelings and circumstances, but adults who speak the truth in love, as they grow up in every way.

Mature Christian love in a good marriage is the result of commitment and work. Helen and I work harder at our marriage than at anything else in the world. For you see, the most childish and immature misunderstanding of all about marriage is simply this: that love is self-sustaining and that a good marriage comes about automatically because two fine, committed young Christians marry one another. If you will get rid of that unbiblical notion, then you will make progress. Marriage is hard work, but you can enjoy it. And you will find that all the work you put into your marriage is worth it, because the one thing you are going to be doing a million years from now is loving. So you'd better get in practice now. And marriage is the best preparation for heaven that I know.

## PRAYERFUL REFLECTION

■ Have you carried childish ideas of love and marriage into your present relationship? Are you ready to "put away your childish ways of thinking" yet? Jot down those parts of your most loving relationship where you have exhibited childish behaviors. Then write a prayer expressing to God what you would like to see happen in the days and months ahead as you let Him *katargeo* your fairy-tale thinking into a growing, maturing concept of love and marriage.

---

---

---

---

---

_____

_____

_____

## PERSONAL RENEWAL

■ This week, try to commit to memory the description of love Paul gives us in 1 Corinthians 13:4-8a. Let his words go deep into your heart and transform the way you think about and live out, love.

*Love is patient and kind. Love is not jealous, it does not brag, and it is not proud. Love is not rude, is not selfish, and does not get upset with others. Loves does not count up wrongs that have been done. Love is not happy with evil but is happy with the truth. Love patiently accepts all things. It always trusts, always hopes, and always remains strong. Love never ends.*

*I urge you therefore, brethren, by the mercies of God, to present your bodies a living and holy sacrifice, acceptable to God, which is your spiritual service of worship. And do not be conformed to this world, but be transformed by the renewing of your mind, that you may prove what the will of God is, that which is good and acceptable and perfect.*

*For through the grace given to me I say to every man among you not to think more highly of himself than he ought to think; but to think so as to have sound judgment, as God has allotted to each a measure of faith.*

*Romans 12:1-3*

# Chapter 6
# Childish Ideas of God and His Will

An astronomer was in conversation with a preacher who wanted the brilliant scientist to think about God. The astronomer just shrugged him off saying, "Preacher, I have a very simple theology: just do good and love your neighbor as yourself." To which the preacher answered, "Yes, and I have a very simple astronomy: 'Twinkle, twinkle, little star.'"

Some of us have this kind of theology, especially when it come to our concepts of God and His will. The question we're really addressing is this, "How does God work to achieve His will in this world?"

If you are like some people I know, you may be thinking, "That's such a theoretical, highfalutin sort of question. It may be good for a philosophy class, but what has it got to do with me and my everyday life?"

I would like to share three true stories with you that illustrate how important it is to be rid of inadequate, immature concepts of God and how He works His will in this world.

• A young couple had taken their baby to the hospital after midnight. Their neighbors called me at 3 o'clock in the morning, and I was there waiting for the couple when they returned home from the hospital. The young mother was wringing her hands, weeping in anguish because her baby was dead. She sobbed, "Oh, my baby! My baby!" Then she said, "I'm sure it must be God's will. . . . But if the specialist had only gotten there in time he could have saved him." Do you hear her agonizing confusion? Did she mean that if the doctor had come in time he could have outmaneuvered and bypassed God's will?

• In 1973, a tragic story appeared on the front pages of every newspaper in the country. A sincere couple in California heard some fly-by-night healer-evangelist preach against using medicine, so they went home and took the insulin away from their fourteen-year-old diabetic son. You know what happened—in a matter of hours he was in a coma, and within a few days he was dead. Then they waited for three days, claiming that God was going to resurrect the boy. Finally the authorities forced them to bury him.

Does this mean that God does or does not want us to take insulin if we have diabetes? Does it mean that God works for healing in the world only by direct action? Without the use of any secondary causes?

If God balances the imbalanced chemistry in your body through some drug and thereby saves your life, or if He gives me good vision through a pair of glasses, or if He gives you new life through heart surgery or the implantation of a pacemaker or through some operation, are these too God's will?

• About ten years ago, an outstanding medical student had finished his residency. He married a fine Christian lady who was also a doctor, and they were planning to be missionaries. Only six weeks after the wedding they went to visit her parents. Her mother who was a former mental patient became deranged, suddenly pulled out a revolver, and shot and killed the young husband. I actually heard people saying that it was God's will. In what sense could such a monstrous thing be described as God's will?

## PERSONAL REFLECTION

■ Have you at any time found it difficult to accept and understand an incident in your life as being "God's will"? Describe some of the confusing situations you've faced in relation to God's will.

_____

_____

_____

_____

_____

_____

How does God achieve His will in this world? This is not some far-out question, believe me. Rather, it is gut-level Christian living, so important that you may need to put away a lot of childish and immature ideas about it. Paul said, "Be babes in evil, but in thinking be mature" (1 Corinthians 14:20, RSV). And you ought to become mature before the disaster happens, because then you will have an anchor in the storms of life, an anchor which holds you steady when "sorrows like sea billows roll," and you feel as though you do not have strength to hold onto anything. Leslie Weatherhead's little book, *The Will of God* (Abingdon), has been a source of comfort to many a struggling Christian. In this chapter, I am using some of his basic ideas which have been most helpful to me.

There are millions of people outside the kingdom of God who resent and hate God because of their misunderstanding about His way of working in our world. And there are millions more in the kingdom who are confused about the subject. I believe our confusion arises because we use the phrase "the will of God" to include several layers of meaning. There are at least three:
- The intentional, perfect will of God,
- The circumstantial, permissive will of God,
- The ultimate will and purpose of God.

## PERSONAL REFLECTION

■ What type of things have you seen happen in the world at large or in your life personally that cause you to wonder—or maybe even resent—how God works out His will?

_____

_____

_____

_____

_____

The intentional will of God is God's perfect will for you and for the world. It is His ideal purpose for your life. Jesus stated it negatively: "It is not the will of your Father who is in heaven that one of these little ones perish" (Matthew 18:14). In God's intention for you, He pours out Himself in fatherly goodness.

It is high time we get rid of all our childish and unbiblical notions which lead us to believe that everything which happens in this world today is the will of God, in the sense that it is what God intends and plans to happen. So much of what occurs is evil and harmful and destructive, and falls within the second meaning—the circumstantial, permissive will of God. But this should not be considered the intentional will of God.

We must realize that the intentional, perfect will of God can be defeated by the will of man for the time being. If this were not true, humans would have no real freedom whatsoever. All evil that is temporarily successful, temporarily defeats the perfect will of God. There are a thousand and one tragedies which are the furthest thing from God's intention for those situations... the starving children of Somalia, the millions of street people in India, the horrors of concentration camps, the 50,000 people who are slaughtered annually on American highways, and the countless victims of child abuse and violence. Or it may be as personal as your being a single person without any real prospects of marriage, or that you flunked a midterm exam. The list is endless. You may call these things evil, or the fruit of human sin, ignorance, folly, and selfishness. You may call these things accidents. You may call them the inevitable consequences of personal and social sin. But do not call them the intended, planned will of God!

There are some people who find consolation in thinking their tragedies are the intentional will of God. But ultimately, there is never any real comfort or support in something that is not true. If you base your support on an idea of God which is untrue, then in your hour of real need you will be left without meaning. You may end up resenting God, and do yourself great emotional and spiritual damage.

## PERSONAL REFLECTION

■ What, if any, confusion do you have regarding the concept of "the intentional, perfect will of God"?

_____

_____

_____

_____

■ Have you ever made a decision that in the end caused you pain? Jot down one or two decisions you've made, believing at the time you were following God's will for your life, only to have things turn out badly in the end.

_____

_____

_____

_____

_____

■ When a decision "goes bad," do you ever doubt God's leading in your life? Why or why not?

_____

_____

_____

_____

■ What do you find to be the most challenging part of knowing and doing the will of God in your life?

_____

_____

_____

_____

The circumstantial or permissive will of God is operative in our fallen cosmos. Paul said, "We know that the whole creation has been groaning in travail" (Romans 8:22, RSV). Not only do we humans have imperfections and infirmities, but the radical defect of imperfection goes through all of nature with its disasters. Sin is so serious that it has caused a radical imbalance and imperfection in the created cosmos. Because of that imbalance, because of human folly and sin, because man's free will creates circumstances of evil that cut across God's plans, there is a circumstantial or permissive will of God.

When an infant accidentally fell out of a fifth-story window, someone asked whether the death of that child was God's will. Do you see how important it is that we get our thinking straight before answering that question? After another tragic accident, I said at the funeral that God never intended it to happen. And I was deluged with calls all week from people who asked, "You didn't mean what you said, did you?" To which I responded, "I certainly did! I cannot say that God intended that accident to happen." I couldn't worship a God like that.

In circumstances surrounding such accidents, God wills that the law of gravity will operate. God's laws and His causes are continuously working. It is God's will that a baby is made out of flesh and blood, not out of plastic or rubber. According to the law of gravity, when flesh and blood tangle with concrete the result is going to be a smashed body. The very law that enables the child to stay on the face of the earth is the same law which can kill. The law is not suspended if we sin or are careless; nor is it suspended if we are the innocent party in an accident.

It is within the circumstantial will of God that the principle in Romans 8:28 is so vital for our Christian lives. Many things which are permitted to happen to us in this world are the price of: (1) a world of reliable laws, where we can count on things, and (2) a world of free moral choices. Certain events happen within God's circumstantial will, but not directly because God intends or wills them. The wonderful assurance of the Scripture is that God will not allow anything to happen to us which by itself can defeat His ultimate purposes or defeat His children.

As Weatherhead so beautifully puts it, "Nothing can happen to you that God cannot use for good." And that puts us on entirely different ground, because it is never the event in itself, but rather the fact that God is at work that makes a circumstance turn out for good. God Himself does not change or undo the nature of a tragedy—the evil of it, the awfulness or pain of it. However, God can work with us, changing the meaning of that event to our total life, working out His will in the circumstance.

Because God can use all things, anything becomes grist for His will and His mill. Therefore, no Christian can ever say, "Well, you see, I wanted to do this, and I wanted to do that, but I was a victim of a terrible home situation, a tragic accident, disease, injustice, loss—so what could I do?" There are no circumstances which are so deadly in and of themselves that they can down the Christian or defeat God— not even death itself. God is never beaten by any possible combination of circumstances.

## PERSONAL REFLECTION

■ Essentially, the concept of "God's permissive will" embraces the truth that "bad things happen to good people." Why is this concept hard for you to accept? Or isn't it?

_____

_____

_____

■ The reverse concept is also true—"good things happen to bad people." Describe a time when you saw someone you perceived as bad experience an apparent blessing. How did you feel about what happened?

_____

_____

_____

_____

_____

■ What conflict, if any, do these two concepts—of "unmerited good" and "undeserved bad"—create in your mind when it comes to understanding God as you know Him?

_____

_____

_____

_____

■ Weatherhead states, "Nothing can happen to you that God cannot use for good." In what ways does your life bear out the truth of Weatherhead's statement? Describe at least one painful circumstance from your own life that God redeemed and used for your ultimate good.

_____

_____

_____

_____

The ultimate will of God can never be finally defeated. Weatherhead uses this very beautiful illustration. Picture some children playing in a tiny mountainside stream. They divert the stream by making little dams of mud and stones, and they float their toy boats in the puddles and ponds. But the stream continues to surge down to the river and the valley. Now picture men building great dams, changing the course of rivers with lakes and locks, diverting their flow. Yet even they cannot prevent the streams from flowing into the sea.

In our lives, so many things—our sins and mistakes, the accidents of history, the sins of others against us—may divert and temporarily defeat God's plans and purposes. But even in new circumstances created by evils, ills, and accidents, God will provide other channels to carry out His ultimate will.

What is meant by the omnipotence of God? It does not mean that by sheer exhibition of power God gets His own way. This would make our freedom an illusion, and moral growth an impossibility. That God has power means He has the ability to achieve His purposes. To say that God is all-powerful means that nothing can happen which will ultimately defeat Him.

With evil intention the establishment of Jesus' day took the innocent Son of God and crucified Him on the cross. Purely from a human standpoint, it was the most heinous crime in history. But six weeks later, Christ's disciples were preaching about that very same death on the cross. God had made man's crime His instrument to save the whole world.

Accidents, disasters, and moral evil create terrible pain. But to those of us who love God, who are called and who cooperate with His purpose, our suffering cannot separate us from His love, or defeat the working out of His purpose in our lives.

Bible scholar William Barclay of Glasgow University was a prolific writer. Barclay's famous commentaries on the New Testament are known around the world and have been translated into many languages. While we would not agree with some of their theological conclusions, they are unexcelled for background material on the New Testament. "How did William Barclay do it?" is a question that has been asked over and over again. Writing newspaper columns, authoring books, appearing on TV programs, working as dean of a college, taking time to be with students and to listen to them—how did he do it? In a manner different than most of us will ever employ.

You see, some years earlier when William Barclay discovered that he was going deaf, he was faced with a decision: should he turn in on himself in self-pity and end his career? What a blow! Would anyone say that deafness was God's intended, perfect will for William Barclay or anyone else? I doubt it. But knowing himself to be within the circle of God's permissive, circumstantial will, and grasping all the power in the promise of Romans 8:28, William Barclay decided that he would make use of his new world of almost total silence. Shut off from all the other sounds of life, he gave himself totally to hearing the inner sounds of God's Word. Even though a hearing aid did help, he would often shut it off in order to be in a world of silence. Instead of self-pity, he wrapped Romans 8:28 around his deafness and used it to work out God's purpose through his life.

May God help each of us to reach a truly biblical understanding of this whole matter. As Paul would say, and I too would affirm:

"Brothers, sisters, think on these things. Be mature in your thinking, because some day the emotional balance and spiritual life of yourself, or of someone else, may depend on your mature understanding of this matter."

## PRAYERFUL REFLECTION

■ Are you facing any difficulties in your own life at present which have caused you to doubt God's omnipotence and love? Freely admit to Him what you are feeling.

Dear God,

_____

_____

_____

_____

■ Then pray this prayer in the quietness of your heart.

*O Lord,*
*I struggle with deep and difficult things in my life.*
*I know from personal experience the agony of trying*
*to discover Your way and Your will for my life.*
*Save me from childish half-truths which can destroy my*
*faith. I pray that You will help me put life together in a*
*mature way—to understand and to work with You in the*
*accomplishing of Your will in my life and in the world.*
*In Jesus' name. Amen.*

## PERSONAL RENEWAL

■ Let the words of Jeremiah 29:11-13 (RSV) reassure you that God is accomplishing His will in your life and in the world.

*"For surely I know the plans I have for you," says*
*the LORD, "plans for your welfare and not for harm,*
*to give you a future with hope. Then when you call*
*upon Me and come and pray to Me, I will hear you.*
*When you search for Me, you will find Me; if you*
*seek Me with all your heart."*

*And it came about that while He was praying in a certain place, after He had finished, one of His disciples said to Him, "Lord, teach us to pray just as John also taught his disciples."*

*Luke 11:1*

*"Pray, then, in this way:*
*'Our Father who art in heaven,*
*Hallowed be Thy name.*
*Thy kingdom come.*
*Thy will be done,*
*On earth as it is in heaven.*
*Give us this day our daily bread.*
*And forgive us our debts,*
*As we also have forgiven our debtors.*
*And do not lead us into temptation,*
*But deliver us from evil.*
*For Thine is the kingdom,*
*And the power,*
*And the glory, forever.*
*Amen.'"*

*Matthew 6:9-13*

# Chapter 7
# Childish Ideas of Prayer

We are continuing to look at God's will, but we are bringing it down now to the place where it affects us the most, in our praying. False and immature concepts of prayer are terribly destructive factors in the lives of Christians who are trying to grow up. And they keep millions of people from even entering the kingdom.

In one of Somerset Maugham's best-known novels, *Of Human Bondage*, there is the story of a little boy named Phillip. Born with a clubfoot, Phillip is crippled and very self-conscious about his deformity. One day he hears that God can do anything if we will only pray and ask Him for it. So before going to sleep one night he looks down at his twisted foot and asks God to straighten it out for him by the next morning. He then falls asleep fully expecting that by the next day his foot will be normal. But when he awakens and pulls back the cover, Phillip discovers that his foot is still misshapen and ugly. He is hurt and disillusioned. The experience is the beginning of his loss of faith.

This kind of story is repeated countless times in the lives of grown-ups. I have spent innumerable hours with people whose faith has been similarly shaken because God didn't answer particular prayers for them. Many times things are made worse for them because well-meaning but ill-informed Christians have encouraged them to pray. They have quoted Scripture verses about God's power and sometimes have gone so far as to practically guarantee that God would answer their prayers.

## PERSONAL REFLECTION

■ Has this been your experience? Have you ever felt like God didn't answer your prayer because you didn't see Him answer it in the exact way or specific time frame you had asked for an answer? How did that experience impact your ability to trust God?

_____

_____

_____

_____

_____

_____

It was this way with Connie, a young adult who had just come through a traumatic divorce. She told me through bitter tears that she had been a gung-ho Christian for many years. She listed many involvements in the life of her church, her faithfulness in daily devotions, her generosity in giving. At work, everyone knew Connie as an outspoken witness for her faith and she had even won several of her coworkers to Christ.

As she talked to me, she still couldn't believe what had happened. Her husband had run around on her and finally left home. She did not believe in divorce and had done everything in her power to hold the marriage together. But here she was—divorced, alone, lonely. Worst of all she was angry at God and utterly confused. God had let her down. Practically everyone in her church had been praying for her marriage. Scores, including her pastor, had said repeatedly that she had nothing to worry about, because a large number of God's people "had agreed in prayer" and were sure God would bring her husband back to her and put the marriage together again. So she was angry not only at God but also at the church and her Christian friends. Connie had been badly hurt and she felt shattered. She sobbed as she told me the whole story.

I could repeat a hundred other incidents just like that. The scenes would be different, the names and details would vary, but the basic scenario would be exactly the same: hurting people—confused, disillusioned, sometimes rebellious and angry—but always with a shattered faith. Why? In a complex world, they had tried to build part of their adult life on the sandy foundation of a childish, simplistic concept of prayer, and their house had collapsed. They were like the builder in Jesus' parable who had not dug deeply enough.

There is a German proverb which says, "Lies have short legs."

Untruths and half-truths just don't go very far. They can carry you for a while, but not for long. Let's dig deeply into this whole question and find some of our immature and inadequate ideas on prayer. And then let's *katargeo* them quickly before they do us irreparable damage.

## PERSONAL REFLECTION

■ Complete the following statements:

*My greatest disillusionment about prayer came when* _____

_____

_____

*My greatest reassurance about prayer came when* _____

_____

_____

■ Are you aware of any untruths or half-truths you may have concerning prayer? What are they?

_____

_____

_____

_____

One of the favorite questions I use in my church membership training class with youngsters is this, "Can God do anything?" Almost always every hand goes up and they all answer, "Of course. He's God, isn't He?" I keep quizzing them, "Are you sure? Absolutely sure? Can you think of anything that God can't do?" After a few minutes of this, there is usually at least one child who begins to catch on to my question. Very hesitantly he will answer, "Well, maybe He can't do anything that's bad or sinful." Then we always have an interesting discussion together as I point out to the children how important it is to have a God who can't do some things.

It is important that we all come to understand the flip side to the verse we hear so often, "With God all things are possible," namely, that with God some things are impossible. This is one of the fundamental differences between the Christian faith and the Moslem religion. Islam says God can do anything and everything. It will accept no limits to His power which is absolute and arbitrary. We

Christians, on the other hand, say that God's power is unlimited except by His own moral nature and by certain self-imposed limitations He has built into His world, including the moral beings He has created. So the best place to begin getting this whole matter straight is to think about some of the things God cannot and will not do.

**PERSONAL REFLECTION**

■ Do you really believe Dr. Seamands' statement, ". . . with God some things are impossible"? Think for a moment before completing this sentence:

*It is impossible for God to* _____

_____

_____

_____

Let us commence with the most obvious impossibility of all, one which is a foundation stone in the Christian doctrine of God. God cannot sin. He cannot do anything evil, for that would go against His own perfect moral nature. Both Hebrews 6:18 and Titus 1:2 speak of a God who cannot lie. So when we repeat our creeds to the effect that we "believe in God the Father Almighty," we do not infer that His might or power include the ability to do wrong. God's power is unlimited, but it is morally conditioned—it is limited by His perfect nature of holy love. God can do anything which is consistent with His own holy self, but He cannot violate His own nature. God can do anything except not be God!

I remember one of my missionary colleagues telling me about his experience with a converted cannibal over in Africa. One day the new convert came by to ask if it might be possible for him to take a brief vacation from being a Christian—just for a few hours—while he went and killed a certain rival chief who was an ancient enemy. He assured the missionary he would be right back afterward to continue his Christian life. Before we laugh at him, let's remember the many times we have all half-consciously wished we could take a similar vacation. The poor ex-cannibal was disappointed when my friend explained to him why that could never be. It was because of who and what God is.

God cannot cease from being God for a while. He cannot act out of character. Thus God cannot lie or sin or commit any moral evil. James taught this in a different connection, "Let no one say when he is tempted, 'I am being tempted by God,' for God cannot be tempted by evil, and He Himself does not tempt anyone. Every good thing bestowed and every perfect gift is from above, coming down from the

Father of lights, with whom there is no variation, or shifting shadow" (James 1:13, 17). John applied this same principle, "God is light, and in Him there is no darkness at all. If we say that we have fellowship with Him and yet walk in the darkness, we lie and do not practice the truth" (1 John 1:5-6). This means God is pure light and there are no dark spots in Him. Therefore, nothing dark or evil can come out of Him. It further means God cannot make a deal with sin: He cannot tolerate it. To do so would be to violate His own moral nature of holy love.

Of course, this also means that from a moral standpoint God cannot change. If anyone is going to do the changing, we will have to. We need to always remember this for it seems to be one of our lifetime battles—trying to change God, trying in some subtle way to pull Him down to our level. Because we love Him and want to have fellowship with Him, we often try to do it on our terms. But God cannot come to terms with us, for that would be contrary to His own nature and that is impossible for God just because He is God—I should say, especially because He is God! God cannot lie, He cannot sin, He cannot act out of character, He cannot do anything which goes against His own pure and perfect moral nature.

## PERSONAL REFLECTION

■ Have you ever blamed God for something bad that happened to you? What did you blame Him for? If evil is contrary to God's nature, then is it possible that you've misplaced the blame? Where should the blame be placed?

_____

_____

_____

_____

_____

■ What difference does it make to you personally that God cannot lie or sin or commit any evil? Write a series of "If . . . then" statements affirming the reality of this impossibility. _EXAMPLES: If God cannot lie, then I can trust Him to do what He says He will do in Scripture. If God cannot commit evil, then He cannot be the one responsible for the abuse I experienced in childhood._

_____

_____

_____

_____

_____

_____

_____

_____

There is a second category of things which God cannot do which bears directly upon this matter of proper perspective in prayer. These acts do not concern His own nature, but the nature of the world He has created. Some would say it is too strong to assert God cannot do these things: they would prefer to say He does not do them only because of the kind of world He has created. But this is the only world that we as humans have to live in and we are the only moral creatures of our kind. So for all practical purposes, since God created us and our world and its laws the way He did, then as far as we are concerned it's the only one we operate in.

To say He could have created it all differently is a lot of theory. The world is as it is, and we are who we are. We and God work within the fallen framework of this world. By creating this kind of a world, God has imposed certain limitations on Himself which, as far as we are concerned, make up some of the things which are impossible with God. Using the same principle we did in the first category, we could say that God cannot do anything which is contradictory to itself.

That may sound complicated, but it really isn't. Do you remember discussing this question when you were a kid: "Can God make a rock so big that He couldn't move it?" Or that old favorite, which is actually another version of the same question,"What happens when an irresistible force meets an immovable object?" The problem here is that you are trying to put contradictory things together when it can't be done. In this world you can't have something that is square and round at the same time, a design shaped like both a rectangle and a triangle, or an object that is black and white at the same time. This is just another way of saying that God made this world to operate according to certain laws. We don't know all those laws; we've been a long time discovering some of them and we've got many more to go. These laws really come out of the character of God Himself and express His inner stability and reliability. That's why we can call our universe a cosmos instead of a chaos.

When we fail to realize this and to reckon with it in our prayers, we are on a collision course and someday could get hurt so badly that our faith itself would be badly dented or even destroyed. Much disillusionment with prayer is caused by childish misunderstanding of how God works in relationship to this world.

Let me use an extreme illustration. Let us say there is a married couple who, though they desire a child very much, have so far not been able to have one. They could pray in several different ways which would, in every case, involve either being able to have a baby or God enabling them to adopt a child. We can't imagine any couple who would pray for God to somehow drop a baby into their laps from heaven. But why not? Can't God do anything? It's not hard to see the foolishness and the falseness in this kind of reasoning.

Let's take this line of reasoning one step further. Let's say that through some tragic accident you have to have your leg amputated above the knee. Would you pray that God would grow a new leg for you? Why not? Doesn't the Bible say, "All things are possible with God?" You would be correct in replying, "God just doesn't do things that way." Certainly in the final resurrection that leg will be fully restored, but not in this life.

Perhaps this is the right place to thank God for all the wonderful discoveries of science and modern knowledge. They have cleared away tons of false information and foolish ideas and have given us true insights into the mysteries of our vast universe. That's why we need never be afraid of any new discovery of science. All facts are God's facts. Today we can be much better, saner, more knowledgeable Christians than ever before, because many wrong ideas once held have been cleared up and we now know more truth. It is truth that sets us free and this is just as true in regard to prayer as it is to everything else.

This in no way means that God is a prisoner of His own universe. God can intervene with higher laws than we know anything about. An airplane does not break the law of gravity when it flies; it supersedes it with a higher law—the law of aerodynamics. God often operates by higher laws which transcend the ones we know about. The miracles of the Bible represent God's freedom to work in this way. But even then there is a certain beautiful congruity, a certain lawfulness about those miracles.

C.S. Lewis in his book, *God in the Dock* (Eerdmans), has a most illuminating chapter on this. He points out that when the devil asked Jesus to turn stones into bread, it was more than a mere temptation to take a shortcut to popularity. It was a typically devilish suggestion, for the devil is essentially a magician.

God works miracles, not magic, for no one makes bread out of stones—not even God. He turns seeds into wheat or corn or rye and out of that we make bread. When Jesus fed the Five Thousand, He didn't take stones from the brook and turn them into bread and fish. He took loaves and made more loaves, fish and multiplied them into more fish. This is what farmers do every year and the fish do in season—produce more bread and more fish. It takes them a long time to do it through the laws of nature. But Jesus Christ, being the Lord of both time and nature, can speed up the process into a few moments. Lewis points out that this kind of fittingness and lawfulness is true of all the miracles. God does not contradict Himself or violate the sacred order which He has built into this world.

**PERSONAL REFLECTION**

■ What have you been taught about "healing" that is miraculous in nature—especially as it relates to physical and/or emotional healing?

_____

_____

_____

_____

_____

■ Have you ever felt disillusioned or disappointed with God because you prayed for supernatural physical or emotional "deliverance" and it didn't happen? Describe your experience. How about deliverance from compulsive or addictive behaviors?

_____

_____

_____

_____

_____

All this leads to a third limitation on the power of God. It comes out of the second and is also self-imposed by the ways He has made this world of things and persons. God cannot violate human freedom. He has created a race of persons with freedom to make choices. He did not create fleshly robots, mechanical beings over which He has complete control. He created human personalities made in many ways like Himself—in His own image—with a spirit akin to His own, beings with self-consciousness and self-determination. Limited, yes, by the kind of world we live in, but with enough freedom to choose so as to be responsible to Him.

Let's think of how God works, regarding our salvation. God desires to save us from our sins, bring us into His very own family as His redeemed children, and change us so we will love and serve Him—and do all this without at any point overriding or overruling our freedom. Yet how can He save us without at the same time destroying the very thing He wants to save? God cannot redeem us by mere omnipotence, by the sheer exercise of His power. That would violate our personhood and destroy what He most desires—our freely given love.

How often I have heard from children and teenagers in the counseling room: "Why doesn't God just make me be good?" But that wouldn't be goodness. It would be slavery, and God is not interested in slaves but in sons and daughters! God will not overpower us into goodness; He can and does work through every possible means to get our attention, to call us, to woo us and win us. But He will never ravish us or violate us as persons.

God cannot save us without the consent of our will. Sometimes we point out such things as the conversion of Saul on the road to Damascus, as if God had simply forced him into submission. Certainly it was a powerful revelation of the living Christ. But I remind you that Paul, writing about it years later said, "I did not prove disobedient to the heavenly vision" (Acts 26:19), plainly implying that in spite of all that display of supernatural power, he still had to give the consent of his will. He could have been disobedient if he had chosen to.

Actually all this leads right to the Cross. There is only one way God can save us and preserve our freedom—the way of suffering love. That was the basis of Christ's appeal to the murderous and rebellious Saul: "Saul, Saul, why are you persecuting Me? . . . I am Jesus whom you are persecuting" (Acts 9:4-5). That's what captured Saul's heart and made him a love slave of Jesus for life. Yes, God can suffer for us, appeal to us, unrelentingly love us. But He cannot force us against our will. He cannot violate our moral freedom.

PERSONAL
REFLECTION

■ It is often not until we've reached the "bottom"—when we feel hopeless and helpless—that we turn to God. What "bottom" did you have to hit in order for God to get your attention?

_____

_____

_____

■ Dr. Seamands states, "God will not overpower us into goodness." To what extent has this been your experience?

_____

_____

_____

_____

■ Step Three of the Twelve Steps of Alcoholics Anonymous describes a process whereby we learn to surrender our will and our lives to God: *Made a decision to turn our will and our lives over to the care of God as we understood Him.* What do you feel when you think about putting your life and your will—every area of your life—into God's hands?

_____

_____

_____

_____

■ John MacArthur describes *trust* as "believing [God] has your best interest at heart." Can you think of any areas of your life where you do not trust God (e.g., your finances, a significant relationship, your health, your need for physical intimacy)? *NOTE: A good way to identify these areas is to ask yourself what you worry about a lot.*

_____

_____

_____

_____

_____

_____

_____

We have gone into considerable detail about all this because it is the basic groundwork for a mature and biblical concept of prayer. Without this understanding, prayer can remain a very childish matter built on a mixture of fantasy and fairy-tale magic. Someday it can even become a dangerous boomerang, returning to badly damage your faith.

It is reported that the saintly George Mueller, that remarkable man of faith whose prayers literally fed and clothed thousands of British orphans, once said, "Prayer, apart from Scripture, is ninety percent illusion." It is all right for children to fantasize and live with some imaginary illusion while they are little, but when they grow up they must put away those things. To fail to do so can result in getting hurt. After seeing the movie *Mary Poppins*, one little girl jumped off her rooftop with an open umbrella.

Let's think again about Connie who we mentioned at the beginning of this chapter. What was the real issue behind Connie's shattered faith? It was the fact that another person's will was involved—her husband's. In such instances we can never guarantee the outcome of our prayers, because God cannot violate that person's power of choice. God actually did answer the prayers of Connie and her church friends. God convicted her husband deeply; he was really miserable and unhappy in his sins. But he would not give them up. He used his very God-given power of choice to say no to God. And a tragic divorce was the result. This incident is like so many involving prayer—it was a mixture of truth and error which we commonly call a half-truth. The trouble with a half-truth is that you can always get hold of the wrong half. This was what happened to Connie and her friends. They prayed in great faith because they knew some great truths:

• God certainly wanted the husband to repent and change his behavior.

• God certainly wanted the marriage to be saved, and therefore,

• God would do everything in His power to bring this about. But they went a step too far when they guaranteed Connie (and themselves) that it had to happen. This was false because they forgot to add one more truth to the three above:

• God cannot force anyone against his will; He will not violate our moral freedom. Therefore, the husband could still refuse to do the right thing and could insist on a divorce. Because they ignored this important basic fact, they ended up with a half-truth which turned out to be very destructive.

In his classic book on doubt, *In Two Minds,* Os Guinness deals extensively with the devastating effects of doubts which arise from faulty ideas about God. He says, "The devil's stock in trade is the world of half-truths and half-lies where the half-lie masquerades as the whole truth" (InterVarsity, p. 47). He also points out, "Poor teaching is the largest single cause of those doubts for which the doubter is not initially responsible. When what is taught is such a distortion of God's Word that doubt is inevitable, the basic responsibility is not the doubter's but the teacher's" (p. 207).

PERSONAL
REFLECTION

■ Can you think of any instances when you used your God-given power of choice to say no to God? What were the consequences of saying no?

_____

_____

_____

_____

_____

■ What are some half-truths you've bought into that ultimately proved to be destructive in your life?

_____

_____

_____

_____

_____

How well I remember a sad instance from our days in India. A brilliant young Methodist missionary, Spirit-filled and fruitful in his service, was stricken with appendicitis. He was about to go to the hospital for an operation when some superspiritual friends persuaded him that it would be a great act of faith and a powerful witness to the non-Christians of the community if he did not submit to the operation, but instead had a healing service and trusted God to heal him. Unfortunately, he agreed to their misguided suggestion. Within a matter of hours his appendix burst and a few days later he was dead. All India mourned the loss of this marvelous young missionary with such a promising future. Here again we see what pain such immature half-truths about prayer can bring.

As in this example and the one in the previous chapter about the parents taking insulin away from their son, many of the worst tragedies occur in the realm of half-truths about healing. I have known people who trusted God to heal their poor vision. They threw away their glasses. Then after weeks of suffering, they had to once again have their eyes tested and put on glasses. The basic issue is not whether God heals in answer to prayer, but *how* God brings about this healing.

It is evident that God's usual way of healing is to use the best of human knowledge and medical skill. Ever since He gave the command to mankind to have dominion over the earth and subdue it (Genesis 1:29), it has seemed as if God would rather wait for humans to do just that, and bring about most of the healing through the use of natural means. This is not to say that God cannot occasionally cut through natural means and heal in supernatural ways. But this is definitely the exception, not the rule. We get into trouble when we try to make the exception the rule. Though people prayed for centuries about some of the great plagues and scourges of mankind, God seemed content to wait until humans achieved enough dominion over His world to find the cures. And so came vaccinations which wiped out smallpox, and insulin for diabetes, and the Salk vaccine for polio, and antibiotics which have saved millions of lives. Why didn't God directly intervene before this? Because that is not the way He works in this world of natural law and secondary causes.

## PERSONAL REFLECTION

■ Today there is an ever increasing number of documented cases in Third World countries where God is intervening in the world of natural law and order and healing people in supernatural ways. Even so, this is still the exception rather than the rule. Why do you think God more often chooses to use natural rather than supernatural means to heal people? Have you ever prayed for supernatural healing in your life? What happened?

_____

_____

_____

_____

_____

_____

Unless we really grow up in our thinking about prayer, we can easily fall into what the Bible calls presumption. A synonym for presumption is audacity. In this act, we overstep our limits and ask God to overstep His. There are at least eleven references in the Bible that refer to the matter of presumption. They are all in the Old Testament with the exception of 2 Peter 2:10. In every case presumption is considered a sin, an affront toward God, an overstepping of our bounds with Him. In several instances in the Old Testament its punishment was death. The psalmist wisely prayed, "Keep back Thy servant from presumptuous sins; let them not rule over me; Then I shall be blameless, and I shall be acquitted of great transgressions" (Psalm 19:13).

When Jesus resisted Satan's temptation to jump from the top of the temple, He was refusing to tempt or test the Father by an act of presumption. Many of our childish and immature prayers, based on half-truths and misquotations of Scripture, come dangerously near to being presumption instead of true faith. We need to grow up into Christ in our ideas of prayer lest we fall into errors which bring dishonor to the name of God.

In Catherine Marshall's book, *Meeting God at Every Turn*, she tells of her two-year bout with tuberculosis. She describes her pilgrimage and how God had to bring her step by step from the "oversimplified presumption of the new pupil" to the place where she saw the difference between "presumption that masquerades as faith and real faith." It was not until she was finally able to pray this prayer that a slow but steady healing came about: "Lord, I understand no part of this, but if You want me an invalid for the rest of my life—well, it's up to You. I place myself in Your hands, for better or for worse. I only ask to serve You."

## PERSONAL REFLECTION

■ When do you think faith becomes presumption? Describe what you think the difference is between faith, presumption, and expecting a miracle. What about the "name-it-and-claim-it" concept—do you feel this is presumption? Why?

_____

_____

_____

We would be remiss if we did not take at least a brief look at the question of unanswered prayer. For while the biblical principles we have described can help us understand most of our situations, there are still many times when we feel as if we have prayed from our highest and best understanding and are still left puzzled and confused. Let's face it—at those times the Bible itself may not seem helpful, for it too is full of unanswered prayers.

■ Moses prayed to enter the Promised Land but died with his request refused.

■ Habakkuk cried from his tower, "O Lord, how long shall I cry and Thou wilt not hear?"

■ The psalmist pled in his depression,"Why are Thou so far from helping me, and from the words of my complaint?"

■ Paul prayed three times that his troublesome physical handicap, his "thorn in the flesh" which was hindering his service for Christ, would be removed. But instead he was promised "sufficient grace" to make the best of it and let it make the best of him.

Leonard Griffith suggests that if some twentieth-century moderns were writing the rest of Paul's biography, it might run like this:

After these things, Paul began to lose interest and fell away from the church. . . . His thorn was there to stay; obviously prayer could not budge it. He read some books on prayer; still it did not seem to work. Perhaps he could get along just as well without praying. Why not? He went back to his trade and made tents. He amassed quite a fortune for those days—before he died. The years grew very tranquil and undisturbed in their slow and equal pace from day to day. It was a great relief to be rid of all the wearing obligations of religion, except, of course, that he was never quite happy (*Barriers to Christian Belief*, Harper, p. 112).

No, the problem is certainly not new. But when it is our personal problem with pain, then we need to find our own personal answers. May I borrow from many of the ancient classics on the subject of prayer and suggest some possible reasons for our unanswered prayers:

■ We do not ask for the right things. How often we don't realize what we are asking for. Paul's words in Romans 8:26 apply here, "For we do not know how to pray as we should." James puts it this way, "You ask and do not receive, because you ask with wrong motives"(4:3). So often we pray for things which, if God did provide, would turn out for our worst instead of our best. God is well aware of what we really need. But we often ask for our wants instead of our true needs. Sometimes God does not answer the want we express in prayer in order that He might answer what He knows to be the real need behind it.

The most classic illustration of this in Christian history is the story of Monica, the mother of St. Augustine. In his *Confessions* he described his mother praying all night that God would block her son from setting sail to Italy. She saw her son going from bad to worse and couldn't imagine what would be in store for him if he went far away from her influence, and especially to Italy with all its licentiousness and alluring splendors. But while she was praying, her son set sail to Italy. It was there he met the mighty preacher Ambrose and fell under the right influences. It was there be became a Christian—in the very place from which his mother's earnest prayers would have kept him. Augustine, understanding this aspect of the mystery of unanswered prayer, later wrote a prayer of thanksgiving: "Thou, in the depth of Thy counsels, hearing the main point of her desire, regarded not what she then asked, that Thou mightiest make me what she ever desired."

PERSONAL
REFLECTION

■ Dr. Seamands reminds us that "Sometimes God does not answer the *want* we express in order that He might answer what He knows to be the real *need* behind it." Has this been your experience? Describe a time when God gave you what you needed rather than what you thought you wanted? Have you ever felt disappointed with God's *provision* in your life? Explain.

_____

_____

_____

_____

_____

_____

• We ask for things we should be taking care of ourselves. I saw a TV evangelist actually using a vending machine to illustrate prayer. If we put our prayers of faith in the coin slot, the answers appear where the merchandise falls out. This is to make prayer like room service and God an eternal bellhop, a celestial errand boy. We must never make our prayers a substitute for what God intends us to achieve by ourselves. There were times when God interrupted the prayers of Moses and of Gideon, and in effect said to them, "Don't speak to Me about these matters; go and speak to the Children of Israel." It was not a time for prayer but for action.

God sometimes has to remind us to keep the division of labor straight—to remember what is His work and what is ours. The writer of the Book of Hebrews often mentioned things that Jesus "learned" by suffering and obedience and discipline. What kind of Christians would we be if everything was accomplished simply by praying for it? We would remain spiritual children living in a fantasy land of magic wands.

Griffith offers this incisive illustration: When a boy asks his father to do his homework because he wishes to play, will the father — assuming he is equal to his son's homework—do it? Not if he loves the lad and cares for his growth of character. The father . . . may encourage him, assist him, stand by him, and see him through but he must not do for the son anything that the boy can possibly do for himself (p. 116).

We often say,"Not our ability, but our availability," which is intended to call attention to the fact that it is all accomplished by His power, not ours. But let us remember that our availability includes putting at God's disposal the best that we have and allowing Him to use it as a channel of His power. And our best is usually hard won and slowly achieved.

## PERSONAL REFLECTION

■ Have you ever asked God to bail you out of a situation, and His answer was to let you work through it on your own? What happened?

_____

_____

_____

_____

_____

■ How do you balance personal responsibility (doing what you can) with childlike dependability on God (letting Him do what only He can do)? Give a personal example of a time you did this.

_____

_____

_____

_____

■ We are not ready for God's answer. The longer I counsel people, the more I respect the matter of timing. *Chronos* is the ordinary word for time used in the New Testament. It's just plain human time, and we get words like *chronology* and *chronometer* from it.

The word used for God's time is *kairos*. It means the right time and the ripe time, like the phrase for the advent of Jesus, "the fullness of the time" (Galatians 4:4). I may spend many hours counseling someone only to discover that it is just not their *kairos* time. The books and tapes I loan them and the sessions we have together just don't seem to be going anywhere. We often talk about it and break off our sessions for a while. Sometimes it is years later that they come back to me and tell me, "Now I understand what you were saying; now it all makes sense to me. I reread those books and they really came alive. Could we talk together again?" This time it's different; progress is amazingly swift, growth rapid. Our prayers had not been answered because the person wasn't ready.

John 5:6 is an amazing verse: "When Jesus saw him lying there and knew that he had already been a long time in that condition, He said to him, 'Do you wish to get well?'" Did it take thirty-eight years of illness to make the man feel so desperate he would finally drop his excuses, quit blaming others, and be ready to believe and obey Jesus?

When I was a youngster I had asthma. It got worse in my teenage years, and by my freshman year in college it was so bad I was unable to take my Spring semester exams. I prayed constantly for healing, others prayed for me, and once I underwent the anointing and laying on of hands for healing. The prayers were never answered.

Years later, in my early morning quiet time, God showed me through one sentence in a devotional book that I needed to have a healing of my memories. This involved forgiving someone on a deeper level than I had ever done before. It took several days of heart searching and prayer. I never even prayed about my asthma problem. I just allowed the Spirit to take care of those resentments and hurtful memories. It's hard to believe, but I haven't had any asthma from that day to this! Yes, a lot of prayer had gone up for my asthma, but I was not ready to receive God's answer until my deeper problem was taken care of. This is true for many areas of unanswered prayer in our lives. There are many things God cannot give us until we are ready for them. The saints have always reminded us that *yes* and *no* are not the only answers to prayer. Many times God gives us the other answer—*wait*.

One characteristic of a child is the inability to wait, a need for instant gratification. People who still have a childish outlook on prayer find it difficult to wait upon the Lord. We are to be "imitators of those who through faith and patience inherit the promises" (Hebrews 6:12). Guinness describes this kind of waiting on God as a kind of suspended judgment. He reminds us that sometimes we may not know why, but we can know why we trust in God who knows why. Thus patience and waiting are signs of a mature relationship with God; they reveal our belief that He is truly trustworthy.

PERSONAL
REFLECTION

■ Psalm 37:3-7a (NASB) reminds us to "Trust in the Lord, . . . Delight yourself in the Lord; and He will give you the desires of your heart. Commit your way to the Lord, trust also in Him, and He will do it. . . . Rest in the Lord and wait patiently for Him." Describe a time when you *didn't* wait for God, but ran ahead of Him. What happened?

_____

_____

_____

_____

_____

■ Now describe a time when you *did* wait. What was the result of waiting?

_____

_____

_____

_____

■ Is there anything at present for which you are having to wait on God? What is it? For you, what is the hardest part of waiting?

_____

_____

_____

_____

■ What does "resting in the Lord" look like to you? Describe the attitudes and activity of resting from your point of view.

_____

_____

_____

_____

_____

_____

■ Relationship. That's a good place to bring this to a close. The great devotional writers of the past believed that there is really no such thing as unanswered prayer if we keep our lives in harmony with God. God always answers prayer in one of two ways: either He changes the circumstances or He supplies sufficient power to overcome them. He answers either the petition or the person.

When you understand this, you have put away an immature view of prayer. Your first interest is no longer the gift, but the Giver.

## PRAYERFUL REFLECTION

■ Write a letter of thanks to God expressing to Him why you are grateful that He doesn't always answer your prayers according to what you ask. Begin your letter in this way:

*Dear God,*

*I want to thank You that all of my prayers aren't answered in the ways I*

*ask because_____*

_____

_____

_____

_____

_____

## PERSONAL RENEWAL

■ Matthew 6:9-13 is best known as "The Lord's Prayer" because Christ gave it to His disciples in order to teach them how to pray. Use the Lord's Prayer this week as a pattern of prayer in your own life. Be especially attentive to the phrase "Your will be done."

*Our Father who art in heaven, hallowed be Thy name. Thy kingdom come. Thy will be done, on earth as it is in heaven. Give us this day our daily bread. And forgive us our debts, as we also have forgiven our debtors. And do not lead us into temptation, but deliver us from evil. For Thine is the kingdom, and the power, and the glory, forever. Amen.*

*"He who is without sin among you, let him be the first to throw a stone at her."*

*Jesus said to her, "Woman, where are they? Did not one condemn you?" And she said, "No one, Lord."*

*And Jesus said, "Neither do I condemn you; go your way. From now on sin no more."*

*John 8:7, 10-11*

*He had to be made like His brethren in all things . . . For since He Himself was tempted in that which He has suffered, He is able to come to the aid of those who are tempted.*

*For we do not have a high priest who cannot sympathize with our weaknesses, but one who has been tempted in all things as we are, yet without sin.*

*Hebrews 2:17-18; 4:15*

*You have forgotten the exhortation which is addressed to you as sons,*
*"My son, do not regard lightly the discipline of the Lord,*
*Nor faint when you are reproved by Him;*
*For those whom the Lord loves He disciplines*
*And He scourges every son whom He receives."*

*All discipline for the moment seems not to be joyful, but sorrowful; yet to those who have been trained by it, afterwards it yields the peaceful fruit of righteousness.*

*Hebrews 12:5-6, 11*

# Chapter 8
# Childhood Confusions
# Versus Adult Distinctions

We have now dealt with several different areas where wrong concepts, left over from childhood, give rise to wrong feelings and actions. In some instances, these came out of hurtful experiences and relationships which left scars on our memories. They needed a special kind of healing experience before their emotional bondage could be broken. There were others which came from immature notions in regard to basic Christian truths. These needed the corrective measure of mature, balanced biblical principles.

Now let us consider some childish confusions and the distinctions we need to make if we are going to conduct ourselves as grown-up Christians.

It has been said of children that they are "the world's greatest recorders but the world's worst interpreters." It's difficult to know just where some of these childish confusions came from, and maybe we don't need to know. But the task still remains of sorting them out so we can put away their childish results.

Among evangelical Christians we find a lot of confusion between *acceptance* and *approval*. This can have its roots in families where parents did not make it plain to their children that disapproval of what they were doing did not mean rejection of them as persons. When a child is being punished for something not approved by his parents, it is easy for him to get the idea that they don't like him or accept him as a person. Thus a kind of mathematical formula is implanted in the youngster:

A Child's Formula for Acceptance & Approval

☺ Approval = ✓ Acceptance
☹ Disapproval = X Nonacceptance/Rejection
🍦 Punishment & Discipline = ☺ Disapproval & Rejection

THEREFORE

☺ Approval = "I am loved and accepted."
☹ Disapproval = "I am not loved but rejected."

**PERSONAL REFLECTION**

■ In what ways does the "Formula for Approval and Acceptance" described above fit the model of discipline your parents exercised in your home?

_____

_____

_____

_____

■ Describe a time when you were disciplined for doing something your parents or another authority figure disapproved of.

_____

_____

_____

_____

■ What kind of relationship do you have with your parents today?

_____

_____

_____

_____

_____

■ What do you find yourself doing as an adult to get love and acceptance from other people? *EXAMPLES: I accommodate other people to such an extent that I don't take care of myself. I refrain from expressing my opinions and feelings out loud.*

_____

_____

_____

_____

_____

■ FOR PARENTS ONLY. Most often we parent our children in the same way in which we were parented. In what ways do you parent like your parents? In what ways are you different?

_____

_____

_____

_____

■ FOR PARENTS ONLY. How do you show your children when they need discipline that you love and accept them even though you don't approve of their behavior?

_____

_____

_____

_____

■ Even as adults we need to know we are loved and accepted in spite of the things we do wrong. What do you think is the difference between unconditional *love* and unconditional *acceptance*? How do you let the people you care about know that your acceptance of them does not depend on your approval of everything they do?

_____

_____

_____

_____

_____

_____

If you are a parent, you would do well to look closely at just how you discipline your children. Be sure to make it crystal clear that while you do not approve of what they are doing, you do accept and love them as your children. You do not approve of their conduct, but you will always love them and accept them regardless of what they do. Make it clear to them that your acceptance of them does not depend on your approval of everything they do.

Sometimes children pick up this confusion from their teachers or other authority figures and even their friends. Wherever it comes from, it can create emotional and marital havoc in immature adults. They tend to then record and register any disapproval—even a suggestion, let alone a criticism—with the old formula of nonacceptance and personal rejection. This is a built-in guarantee of personal hang-ups, interpersonal blowups, and spiritual breakups.

It is also the surest way to become a pharisaical Christian. When we carry within us this confusion, it means that we cannot accept and love ourselves unless we can approve everything we do. It follows then—since we treat our neighbors as we treat ourselves—that we shall surely apply this same childish formula to them. When this gets mixed in with a spirit of legalism and a religion which consists mainly of prohibitions and regulations, the result can be especially deadly.

Jack came to see me regarding what he called "a personal family matter." It turned out that he was upset because his brother Joe had walked out on his wife and children after almost twenty years of marriage. The brothers had been very close and Jack felt hurt over Joe's behavior. But what was really bothering him was his confusion over what his attitude should be toward Joe. He had not invited him to his house or even spoken to him for more than a year. Now Joe had recently written and asked if he might come for a visit. Jack was afraid that if he was friendly to Joe, he might give him the idea that he approved of what Joe had done. Or the people in his church might think that he approved of divorce. So he hadn't even replied to Joe's letter. He kept telling me that he knew his feelings were wrong, but he just couldn't help it. "That's the way I was raised," he said, "and I simply cannot lower my moral standards for anyone—not even my brother."

This same dilemma could be duplicated under many different circumstances. Some Christians are afraid to be friendly or even to show ordinary kindness to a sinner for fear the person might get the idea they approve of his sins. There are entire churches who suffer from this confusion. Their attitude is, "We must make sure people know where we stand on this issue." The same personal problem that Jack had is worked out on a group scale. In both instances, it reveals a deep childish insecurity. It is possible to hold the highest moral standards and at the same time be accepting and loving toward those who have violated those standards. The person who feels shock and shows rejection toward those whose behavior he disapproves of is not revealing his own high moral standards. Rather, he is revealing a fearful and insecure area of his own emotions which he has never dealt with. He desperately needs to put away childish confusion and grow up into Christ.

## PERSONAL REFLECTION

■ Have you ever struggled with conflictive feelings similar to those expressed in Jack's scenario? When? How have you learned the balance between "hating the sin" yet "loving the sinner"?

_____

_____

_____

_____

■ Have you ever felt like an "outcast" in the church because of a sin you committed that became public knowledge? Explain what happened.

_____

_____

_____

_____

_____

■ Consider the story of the Woman Caught in Adultery in John 8:1-11. Are the leaders and people of the church you attend more like the Pharisees or like Jesus? Explain.

_____

_____

_____

_____

_____

The process of emotional and spiritual maturing begins by looking at Christ's clear-cut distinction between acceptance and approval. He was so filled with confidence and inner security that He could walk with deep compassion among the publicans and sinners, gluttons and wine-bibbers, thieves and harlots. Yet not once did He ever lower a standard so that anyone might think He was approving of their behavior. This is what the Pharisees accused Him of, but that was only the projection of their own problems onto Him.

The way He dealt with the promiscuous Samaritan woman at the well (John 4:5-42), or the cheating IRS official, Zaccheus (Luke 19:1-10), or the woman caught in the act of adultery (John 8:3-11) gives us a pattern to follow. His words to the woman caught in adultery are the perfect balance of acceptance and approval—"Neither do I condemn you; go your way; from now on sin no more." Here is loving acceptance and redemptive disapproval, personal compassion and moral challenge, beautifully put together by Christ so that distinctions are not blurred.

Many of us will never feel any real peace with God about our own personal salvation until we break the stranglehold of this childish confusion. God does not wait to accept us and love us until He can approve everything about us. If He did, we would all be hopelessly and eternally lost. And if He doesn't wait—with His high and holy standards—why should we wait to accept ourselves and others?

## PERSONAL REFLECTION

■ In what ways, if any, have you been trying to "be good enough" to merit God's acceptance and approval? *NOTE: Oftentimes the subconscious half-truths we believe about God keep us running the treadmill of spiritual performance. EXAMPLE: "If I tithe regularly and serve in the church, God will never withhold his blessing from my life."*

_____

_____

_____

_____

■ Do you think you can ever do anything *so bad* or anything *so good* that God will love and accept you more than He does already? Why?

_____

_____

_____

_____

■ How well do you know yourself? Are you able to accept yourself as you are? What part(s) of yourself do you find difficult to accept? Why?

_____

_____

_____

_____

■ Do you see yourself as a person who is able to accept other people? Have you ever struggled with being overly critical or judgmental of others? Give an example.

_____

_____

_____

_____

_____

It is James who tells us to consider it a joy when we fall into various temptations. He even goes so far as to say that the man who endures temptation is blessed. However, that is not our usual view of the matter, and with some people it is made much worse by a fundamental confusion between temptation and sin. Let us look carefully at Scripture and some practical aspects of temptation so that we will not fall prey to Satan's slimy suggestions which keep us feeling guilty and under condemnation.

First, let us forever fix in our minds that everybody experiences temptation. Dante had an allegorical picture of the Christian life as a journey in which a man climbed up a winding mountain road. When he began the journey, he was a young man. After he had climbed a short while, a snaring wolf leaped out of the bushes and tried to tear him to pieces. To Dante this was the wolf of lust, of bodily passion, and represented major temptation of a young person.

As he climbed higher and came into middle life, a giant tiger sprang on him. This was the tiger of pride, and represented the great temptation of middle age—pride of position, of name, and of status. Finally, near the top , at the time of old age, a great, hairy-maned lion came bounding after him. This was the great temptation of the later life—money and financial security.

In his classification of the three great temptations of life the point Dante was trying to make is this: There is no level of Christian life where you will be free from temptation. There is no person, however Spirit-filled, however saintly and mature, who will not face temptation of some kind.

Many people who seek counsel on the deeper life mistakenly think that if they can just reach a high level of spiritual experience, they will not have to face temptations anymore. The New Testament takes the history and geography of the Children of Israel and uses them as a symbolic picture of our spiritual experiences. For example, the Israelites in Egypt stand for the slavery and bondage of sin; the

## THREE GREAT TEMPTATIONS OF LIFE

miracle of the Red sea represents our salvation and deliverance; the journeys are the normal growth of the soul; the forty years in the desert picture the self-filled, carnal Christian, defeated and discouraged; the Jordan represents the place of full surrender; and the Promised Land of Canaan represents the higher level of Spirit-filled living.

What was the primary activity that characterized the life of God's people under Joshua in Canaan? Warfare. They had entered the land, but now they were to possess all of it! The whole Book of Joshua is the story of great warfare in possessing the land. At every level in your Christian life you will face temptation. Because you are a free moral agent, your power of choice is never taken from you. God never changes you from human to vegetable or animal, or into a moral and spiritual robot. As Oswald Chambers so often said, "God can give us pure hearts in an instant, but He cannot quickly give us Christian character." That takes time and can come only through a series of right moral choices.

Temptation is the proving ground of those choices and no one is exempt, not even our Lord Himself.

## PERSONAL REFLECTION

■ Every one of us experiences temptation. Giving into temptation begins with a series of small compromises (i.e., "Well, maybe doing it just this once won't hurt me."). What are some areas of life in which it is easy for you to compromise?

_____

_____

_____

_____

_____

_____

■ Think of a time when you gave into a temptation. Describe the series of compromising choices you made along the way which ultimately led to your giving into the temptation.

_____

_____

_____

_____

_____

_____

■ Why do you think God doesn't automatically cure us of our tendency to yield to temptation when we commit our hearts and lives to Him?

_____

_____

_____

_____

Still this false and childish fantasy persists and some respond, "Yes, I know all that. But surely if I am truly filled with the Spirit, I would not undergo such strong temptations." Where did this idea come from? Surely not from the Word of God and certainly not from the biographies of the saints. They freely admitted their struggles with all kinds of temptations.

Let us look at the passage in James 1:13-14: "Let no one say when he is tempted, 'I am being tempted by God.'" No, the temptation hasn't come from God. Then from where? Read on: "But each one is tempted when he is carried away and enticed by his own lust."

Now the word *lust* is not a good translation for today. In the 1600s, lust meant the whole range of human desires. Nowadays, we have come to use it only in a sexual sense. For example, this same Greek word is used in Luke 22:15 where Jesus Himself said, "I have earnestly desired to eat this Passover with you." It is also used in Matthew 13:17, where Jesus said, "Many prophets and righteous men desired to see what you see." Obviously the word can mean a desire or longing which is good as well as bad. In James, the word simply refers to what we would call today our inborn natural urges—natural desires, such as hunger for food, the desire for sex, or for recognition or companionship. So we should reread it, "Each one is tempted when he is carried away and enticed by his own desire." (In Greek "carried away" is a term used for fishing, the lure of bait, and "enticed" refers to a hunting trap.)

Now follow it carefully: "Then when lust—or desire—has conceived, it gives birth to sin. And when sin is accomplished, it brings forth death." It takes two to conceive in order to give birth to sin. What are the two? The person's natural desire plus the satanic suggestion, the temptation. So on the one hand we have a natural basic desire, of itself God-given; and, on the other hand, we have the evil temptation, the bait, the trap, the satanic suggestion to misuse that drive, to pervert it and fulfill it in an unlawful and improper manner. But remember the two have not as yet come together. They have not as yet conceived, that is, been joined. The two have not become one; they are still separate.

What is it that can either keep them apart or allow them to come together, conceive, and give birth to sin? Your will! As long as your will says, "No, I will not allow these two to come together; I will that they stay apart," it doesn't matter how strong the desire or how alluring the bait and the temptation, you have not sinned.

A very crude illustration: I have been working out in the yard. It's nearing noontime; I don't need to look at my watch. My stomach has been telling me the time in no uncertain terms. I am hungry; I look up and see an apple tree. Some luscious apples stare me in the face. I'm hungry; I would like to eat an apple; my mouth even waters. So I go over and am about to take one. But on closer inspection I see that the tree is not in my yard; it's in my neighbor's yard and so belongs to him. Now I'm hungry and my desires want me to eat. I am tempted, but I say no; my will comes between the hunger and the apple. I have been tempted. I have not sinned. My will has prevented a joining, a conjunction of the two. If my will would assent, then the two would come together and sin would result.

This is a simple illustration, and for some matters too simple. But it illustrates the main point. Now transfer this same idea over to other areas of temptation, say a sexual desire or the desire for recognition or belonging. All these are basic, good in themselves, God-given desires. To have the desire is no more sinful than when your mouth waters at the apple. But the secret is in what you do with the evil suggestion. If you will refuse to toy with it, you are in the clear. "You can't keep the birds from flying over your head, but you can keep them from nesting in your hair!" Temptation is not sin. A thought of evil is not sin, but allowing it to settle down until it becomes evil thinking is sin. Having the desire is not sin; accepting the evil suggestion to fulfill that desire in the wrong way is sin.

Brent, a college youth, came to counsel with me. After listening to his camouflage of so-called intellectual difficulties he was having with the Christian faith, I asked, "Why don't you tell me what's really bothering you?" He did. He was angry with God. "Why?" I asked. "What did He do to you?" He replied, "That's the problem; it's what He didn't do for me. Last year during Spiritual Emphasis Week I asked Him to take away my sexual desires. The struggle was too great, so I asked Him to remove them."

Brent's real problem was that he had never gotten clear in his mind the distinction between temptation and sin. We spent a long time together until he saw it clearly. When he was able to see the foolishness of his anger against God, he could be restored in his Christian walk. Years later I had the privilege of performing Brent's marriage ceremony to an attractive Christian young lady. At the reception he whispered to me, "I'm sure glad God didn't answer that prayer." I laughingly replied, "Amen!"

Don't ask God to take away your sexual desire, or your ambitions, or to remove your temper from you. He cannot answer these prayers. He can and will give you self-control over your sexual desires. He can enable you to have one all-consuming ambition—His glory. And He can cleanse and redirect your temper so that, like Jesus, you will get angry at the things you ought to get angry at. Know the difference between temptation and sin.

## PERSONAL REFLECTION

■ Dr. Seamands describes the conflict that arises within us when our natural urges or desires cannot be met in normal ways—we tend to find inappropriate ways to get those needs met. Listed below are some basic human needs. Describe some "legitimate" and some "lustful" means *you* might take to get these needs met. Be rigorously honest with yourself.

**The Need for Belonging.** _____

_____

_____

_____

**The Need for Financial Security.** _____

_____

_____

_____

**The Need for Significance.** _____

_____

_____

_____

**The Need for Intimacy.** _____

_____

_____

_____

**The Need for Sex.** _____

_____

_____

_____

**The Need for Love and Acceptance.** _____

_____

_____

**The Need for Food.** _____

_____

_____

_____

**The Need for Shelter/Physical Safety.** _____

_____

_____

_____

**The Need for Recognition.** _____

_____

_____

_____

**The Need to Feel Personally Competent.** _____

_____

_____

_____

■ Are you aware of any areas in your life where you seem to repeatedly fall prey and succumb to certain temptations, no matter how much you exert your will and want to say no? What are they?

_____

_____

_____

_____

_____

*NOTE: You may be dealing with an addiction. If this is the case, you may find that all the self-control in the world still isn't enough to help you overcome the cycle of sin that seems to persist. The 12-Step principles of Alcoholics Anonymous offer you a process whereby you can begin to experience freedom from the cycle of sin and shame that is so much a part of addiction. See the list of "Support Group Resources" in Appendix Two for additional help.*

The confusion between being hurt and being harmed is another hangover from our childhood and teenage years. It is almost impossible for a small child to understand this difference. Whatever the circumstances or the motive behind it, anything which causes pain to a child is seen as a hurt. A parent or friend might do something only by accident, and he might feel terrible about it afterward. It makes no difference to the child—it hurts and therefore he cries.

As we grow up, we slowly begin to see the difference. When I used to wrestle with my dad, sometimes he would accidentally hurt me. I remember looking at his eyes. If I saw pain there I knew he hadn't meant to do it, and even though sometimes my pain was severe and I wanted to cry, I didn't. I didn't realize then that I was learning an important lesson.

Of course, I was fortunate because my dad is a wonderful Christian man. He recently celebrated his ninetieth birthday by returning for a brief visit to India where he had spent forty years as a missionary.

But what about a family where there is really no difference between hurt and harm—where discipline and punishment, alcohol and anger, put-downs and throw-downs all get mixed together so that when someone is hurt he is also harmed? It can be difficult for a person out of that background to make this distinction. He may have memories that need healing and a whole response system which needs reprogramming before he can really become mature in Christ.

For the maturing process requires discipline. It is a sign of God's love and concern for us. "Those whom the Lord loves He disciplines. . . . God deals with you as with sons; for what son is there whom his father does not discipline? . . . He disciplines us for our good, that we may share His holiness" (Hebrews 12:6-7, 20). This means that God does not hesitate to hurt us if this is necessary to help us become mature sons and daughters of His.

He will hurt us but He will never harm us. He will hurt us if that is necessary to wean us away from dependence on feelings to total dependence upon Him. He will hurt us if that is necessary to wean us from self-sufficiency to total dependence on Him. This means He will sometimes hurt us by allowing us to undergo falls and failures until we realize that apart from Him we can do nothing or be nothing. God is not afraid to hurt us, but the hurt is always to heal and help us, never to harm us.

Perhaps I can best illustrate this by an intimate and painful page from our family life. Our son, Steve, was born while we were missionaries in India. Helen and I saw immediately that he had a twisted clubfoot. The crucial time for treating this deformity is the first forty-eight hours after birth, but we were 500 miles from a hospital having an orthopedic physician—a difficult two-day journey. It was almost a month before we could travel with Steve to the Presbyterian hospital where his little foot could be placed in a plaster cast.

Because that clubfoot got a month's head start, to straighten it took several years and required three painful operations.

I'll never forget the day when our wonderful orthopedic surgeon in Lexington, Kentucky called Helen and me in. He placed a bottle in my hands. It was all wrapped in cotton, so it would be soft but firm. He said, "Daddy, I'm going to give you a tough job. If we're going to help this foot heal after the operation and keep it from reverting to the old twist, you're going to have to turn it back the opposite way."

Every evening there were some traumatic minutes in our family. Helen had to hold Steve—he was just a toddler—and I had to take his foot and put it over the bottle and twist it as far back in the opposite direction as it was turning in the wrong direction.

You can imagine Steve's response—his cries of pain. Sometimes when he'd plead with me to stop and I didn't, he would scream, "Daddy, I hate you!" My stomach would churn. I'd get sick of the whole business.

But years later, when I saw him playing Little League baseball, when I sat on the sidelines of the college tennis courts and watched Steve and his cousin win the tennis doubles tournament three years in a row, I said, "It was worth it." Today when I see him walk with no noticeable limp, I say again, "It was worth it."

In the coming days your Heavenly Father may say to you, "We are now going to get down to the business of straightening you out, until you grow up in every way into Christ." When He does this, it will hurt. But do not let any childish experiences throw you into confusion. Always keep in mind this important distinction: God may hurt you, but He will never harm you.

## PERSONAL REFLECTION

■ For those reading this chapter who've been seriously abused in the past, or repeatedly hurt in the present, the distinction between God *hurting* you, but never *harming* you may be hard to grasp at an emotional level. Express how you feel about this concept.

_____

_____

_____

_____

_____

■ What are some of the painful experiences of your life that God has used to bring about a positive change or new level of emotional or spiritual maturity in your life?

_____

_____

_____

_____

■ Any "dependency" we hold on to in this life other than dependency on God will be tested. The road to spiritual maturity is one of learning complete dependence on God. How have you learned through firsthand experience that God ALONE is enough? What are some other things (including people) on which you have been dependent?

_____

_____

_____

_____

## PRAYERFUL REFLECTION

■ The following poem by Dale Martin Stone so wonderfully captures the point that "God may hurt us in order to help us, but never to harm us."

### The Shaping of a Disciple

When God wants to drill a man, and thrill a man,
   and skill a man,
When God wants to mold a man to play for Him
   the noblest part,
When He yearns with all His heart to build so great and
   bold a man

> That all the world shall be amazed, then watch God's
> methods, watch His ways!
> How He ruthlessly perfects whom He royally elects;
> How He hammers him and hurts him, and with mighty
> blows converts him,
> Making shapes and forms which only God Himself can
> understand,
> Yet God bends but never breaks when man's good He
> undertakes;
> When He uses whom He chooses, and with every purpose
> fuses
> Man to act and act to man, as it was when He began;
> When God tries His splendor out, man will know what
> He's about!

■ Of the three "adult distinctions" Dr. Seamands discusses in this chapter, which one impacts your life most significantly at this point in time? (Check one.)

❑　The distinction between *acceptance* and *approval*.
❑　The distinction between *temptation* and *sin*.
❑　The distinction between *hurt* and *harm*.

■ Write a prayer expressing to God why you are thankful He is a God who accepts you even when He can't approve of your behavior; who never judges you for being tempted, only for giving in to sin; who will never harm you, only allow you to experience hurt that can heal and help you.

_____

_____

_____

_____

## PERSONAL RENEWAL

■ Whether you're finding it difficult to feel acceptable to God, yourself or others; struggling with sin; or going through a painful time of change—draw strength this week from Paul's letter to the church in Ephesians 3:16-20 (NCV).

> *I ask the Father in His great glory to give you*
> *the power to be strong inwardly through His*
> *Spirit. I pray that Christ will live in your hearts*
> *by faith and that your life will be strong in love*

*and be built on love. And I pray that you and all God's holy people will have the power to understand the greatness of Christ's love—how wide and how long and how high and how deep that love is. Christ's love is greater than anyone can ever know, but I pray that you will be able to know that love. Then you can be filled with the fullness of God. With God's power working in us, God can do much more than anything we can ask or imagine.*

*And I, brethren, could not speak to you as to spiritual men, but as to men of flesh, as to babes in Christ. I gave you milk to drink, not solid food; for you were not yet able to receive it. Indeed, even now you are not yet able, for you are still fleshly. For since there is jealousy and strife among you, are you not fleshly, and are you not walking like mere men?*

*For when one says, "I am of Paul," and another, "I am of Apollos," are you not mere men? What then is Apollos? And what is Paul? Servants through whom you believed, even as the Lord gave opportunity to each one. I planted, Apollos watered, but God was causing the growth. So then neither the one who plants nor the one who waters is anything, but God who causes the growth.*

*1 Corinthians 3:1-7*

# Chapter 9
# Childish Dependency on Feelings

The word that the Apostle Paul used for "childish," *nepios,* is seldom used in Scripture. In each case it suggests an adult who displays the irresponsible characteristics of a child, an adult whose development has been arrested. This same word is used in Hebrews 5:11-14, condemning those who are still needing to be spoon-fed or nursed on milk because they are babies (babyish). Paul used it in writing to the Corinthians: "And I, brethren, could not speak unto you as to spiritual men, but . . . as to babes" (1 Corinthians 3:1). He followed this with a catalog of their babyish actions.

PERSONAL
REFLECTION

■ Can you think of any adults you know who display irresponsible characteristics of a child? Describe the behaviors you see in them that seem irresponsible. How do you feel when you are with these people?

_____

_____

_____

_____

_____

_____

■ Now take a look inward. Do you see any of the characteristics you listed in the previous question as being true of yourself? Make a list of them. Then using a chronological age, state how "old" (or young) you see yourself as being emotionally.

_____

_____

_____

_____

_____

■ The term "adult children" has become well-known in recovery circles today. In his book, *When I Grow Up . . .* (Recovery Publications, p. 46), author Ron Ross describes some common behaviors that characterize "adult children." Which of the following characteristics are true of you at present? Check all that apply.

### Common Behaviors of Adult Children

❑ We are incapable of building and maintaining enduring, meaningful, and intimate relationships with God, ourselves, or others.

❑ We find it difficult to trust ourselves or others in a deepening fashion; thus, it is hard for us to live by faith.

❑ We do not possess the skills or vocabulary necessary for the healthy communication of feelings, preferences, ideas, or needs.

❑ We do not know how to manage the inevitable stresses of life; we cannot easily play, relax, or rest.

❑ We do not possess the skills necessary to understand God's will in our lives.

❑ We are resistant to change.

❑ We are rigid and inflexible in our thoughts and actions.

❑ We lack the ability to grow spiritually and emotionally.

❑ We do not know how or where to seek help or to offer help to others.

❑ We do not know how to handle adult responsibilities and relationships.

❑ We often feel that we do not belong anywhere.

❑ We have difficulty developing healthy beliefs, morals, and values.

❑ We have a strong need to be in control.

❑ We have difficulty following projects through from beginning to end.
❑ We feel guilty when we stand up for ourselves.
❑ We give in to others instead of taking care of ourselves.

*NOTE: You may not necessarily exhibit all of the characteristics prevalent in adult children, but most likely you will see at least three of the characteristics that apply to your life.*

This reference to infantile behavior is clearly not a matter of chronology, since all the passages were written to adults. Such babyishness does not go away by itself with the mere passing of time. Age will not necessarily fill you with maturity—just wrinkles! Therefore, babyish behavior has to be dealt with very decisively, says Paul. Why? Because it results from a defective form of love. If we are to find mature love as described in 1 Corinthians 13, we must put this babyishness out of our lives.

The chief characteristics of toddlers are their total self-centeredness and their inability to wait for anything. Little children want the time lag between desire and fulfillment to be very short. They demand immediate gratification. They are also almost totally dependent on feelings.

Many adults are babyish in these very same ways—self-centered, demanding immediate gratification of desires, and overly dependent on feelings.

Feelings are important, and there is a central place in Christian religion for the emotional life. The fruit of the Spirit is love, joy, peace, and all three of these include feelings. Christianity is not a form of stoicism. It in no way relegates the emotions to a second-class status, but recognizes that wholeness must include the emotional life. One of the characteristics of life in the Holy Spirit is the free flow of all that is deepest in the human personality. The Spirit frees us to experience and express our emotions.

## PERSONAL REFLECTION

■ Of the three characteristics Dr. Seamands uses to describe childish adult behavior—self-centeredness, need for immediate gratification of desires, dependency on feelings—which one(s) crop up most often in your life? Describe two or three ways in which you've displayed any or all of these characteristics in the recent past.

_____

_____

_____

_____

_____

_____

_____

_____

■ Do you agree with Dr. Seamands that childish behavior results from a defective form of love? Why? What type of love do you think he's talking about?

_____

_____

_____

_____

The way you express your feelings in other areas of life will show up in your Christian life. If you have difficulty with feelings in your general living, you are not going to be a totally changed person emotionally after you are converted or filled with the Spirit. You will have similar difficulties with feelings in your Christian life. Some people have more trouble along these lines than others do. I think Paul's young disciple, Timothy, was sensitive, prone to depression and discouragement. When he felt low, Paul would have to "stir him up to remembrance" and get him going again.

Some people suffer disillusionment because they believe their Christian experiences should alter their basic personality patterns and temperaments. God is not out to change your fundamental personality structure. He can use you to His glory; He wants you just exactly the way you are. In the play, _Green Pastures_, Noah in his great moment of acceptance and surrender says, "Lord, I ain't much, but I's all I's got!" That is a very profound statement. The sooner you rejoice in who you really are, the better. For God wants to use you—the unique and irreplaceable you.

We all have problems in certain areas of our lives. As we vary in talents and in gifts, so we vary in our difficulties. However, most people have some problems with their temperament or disposition. Therefore, one of the healthiest things a new Christian can do is to take a good look at himself, accept the basic facts about his personality and not berate himself because he isn't like someone else.

Our feelings are the most variable and the most unreliable part of our makeup. They are mysterious. They are inexplicable. You cannot directly create a feeling and then command it at will. Feelings are dependent on many factors, some known, some unaccounted for. The saints of old recognized this. The sixteenth-century French saint, Fenelon, wrote about "dry spells," those rather feelingless periods in the Christian life. He offered a list of things that can produce these dry moments. Some of the items sound very spiritual, but right in the center of the list is this one: "They also may be caused by well-meaning guests who stay too long in your home." (And you wondered if you were sinful for feeling the same way!) He had the sense to see that feelings are created by a great variety of causes. For example, do you sometimes awaken in the morning in a mood that is completely different from the way you felt the night before? And you can't figure out any good reason for it?

This is why it is so utterly childish to let our feelings control us and, above all, to let them become the thermometer of our spiritual health. It is only a small step from this control to guilt and resentment and thinking something is wrong with us because we have not had a particular kind of experience or feeling. For then we begin to compare and we "if only," wanting to be someone we're not.

PERSONAL
REFLECTION

■ Can you separate out behavior characteristics that are common to your basic personality and temperament patterns from those that are the result of emotional and spiritual immaturity? How do you see the "unique and irreplaceable you" that God created and loves? Write all that you know about your basic personality and your innate abilities.

_____

_____

_____

_____

_____

■ What parts of your personality do you find most difficult to accept? What do you like most about who you are?

_____

_____

_____

_____

■ Not until you know and accept yourself—the God-created you—can you accept other people for who they are. Do you agree with this statement? Why?

_____

_____

_____

_____

■ Think of one or two recent instances when your feelings controlled your behavior. Write down what happened.

_____

_____

_____

_____

_____

■ James Dobson wrote a book entitled _Feelings—Can You Trust Them?_ What have you come to believe about the reliability of feelings as they relate to your experience?

_____

_____

_____

_____

Now let us think about some areas of our Christian lives where we need to _katargeo_ our babyish dependency upon feelings, and to find a mature and balanced wholeness of Christian living.

Some people are dependent on feelings as the basis for their assurance of salvation. I doubt if any other subject brings as many people to the pastor as the matter of feelings in relationship to salvation. Because feelings are so variable and unreliable, it is dangerous to rely on them in this way. This does not mean that the Spirit's witness with my spirit that I am His child will not deeply involve my feelings and emotions, because it certainly will. But feelings must never be made central. They are not meant to take first place in assurance, and if you put them there, you are doomed to be an unhappy and unstable Christian who does not follow the divine order of things.

This divine order was stated so simply by David, "O taste and see that the Lord is good" (Psalm 34:8). You cannot reverse that and say, "O see and taste." Experiencing before tasting is impossible. The truth of God's promises in Scripture comes first, those promises attested to by the life and death and resurrection of Jesus. The truth as seen in the person of Jesus Christ has to be accepted, acted on , submitted to, and believed in before it produces the right feelings. The emphasis in the Bible is on grasping the truth, on establishing the relationship which produces the feelings. That is the divine order. Fact, faith, and feeling. Taste and see—faith, belief, acceptance, grasping, and then the seeing and the feeling that the Lord is good.

The surest way to become a defeated, morbid, unstable Christian is to always ask yourself: "Well, how do I feel?" To base your relationship to God on the condition of your feelings is a certain sign of spiritual babyhood. The sure road to maturity is to learn to live above moods and feelings. This is going to require discipline. And it will require particular effort for feeling-centered individuals who have never learned in other areas of life to seek truth before feeling.

I like the suggestion which comes to us from our dear missionary friend from India, Sister Anna Mow. She gives her formula for those blue days when you feel depressed and condemned, and are prone to doubt your salvation because you just feel so bad. On those blue days, Anna Mow talks to herself. And that's a good idea. I do that occasionally too, simply because I enjoy intelligent conversation! This is what Anna says to herself when she is not feeling good:

- ❏ Did I get enough sleep last night?
- ❏ Have I hurt someone, intentionally or inadvertently?
- ❏ Do I feel resentment or self-pity?

If all is well in these three areas and Anna can find no reason for her spiritual indigestion, she just throws back her head and laughs at herself. And what a wonderfully contagious laugh she has, as she says to herself, "All right, Anna Mow, you stay here in the blues if you want to. I'm going on with the Lord."

There is a profound truth in Anna Mow's simple formula. You are not just your feelings. At any given moment you are greater than the sum total of your thoughts and feelings. Your selfhood is above and beyond any feelings you may be having, and you can transcend your feelings. One of the most important steps of growth in the Christian life is to reach the place where you affirm this truth about yourself.

I remember when our son did it. After his senior year in high school, he sold books door to door in a distant state. Our phone bill that summer was absolutely phenomenal, because when things weren't going right, Steve would get on the phone—collect, of course. And we could tell from the first word if he was down. I remember saying to him on the phone again and again, "Steve, you are at the age where you have to face one of the greatest decisions in your life: Are you going to take control of your life and run your feelings? Or are your feelings going to take control of you and run your life?" He went away as a boy. He came back a young man because he made a fundamental decision about himself that summer.

It is a great turning point when you decide that you are going to run your life. Some of you are still on the cradle roll because you have never made that decision.

The disciples said, "Lord, teach us to pray." Jesus did not answer, "Well, now, when you feel like praying. . . . " No. He said, "When you pray, say, 'Our Father.'" You may say, "But, Lord, I don't feel like saying, 'Our Father.'" "The kingdom of heaven," said Jesus, "suffers violence, and violent men take it by force"(Matthew 11:12). It is not Christian merely to say what you feel; it is Christian also to say and to pray what you know you ought to feel.

E. Stanley Jones said that sometimes you have to feel yourself into a new way of acting, but at other times you have to act yourself into a new way of feeling. Faith is basically action. It is belief acted upon and lived out that in time produces a certain kind of feeling. That is God's order. Don't try to reverse it or you will be a childish Christian, unstable in all your ways.

## PERSONAL REFLECTION

■ Have your feelings ever floundered in regard to your personal salvation? What do you think caused you to doubt the assurance of salvation? What is the basis of your salvation?

_____

_____

_____

_____

_____

■ If you grew up in a home where feelings were discounted or rarely expressed, you will find it difficult to trust what you feel. Yet sometimes the Holy Spirit speaks truth to us at the feeling level and if we discount or dismiss feelings we can miss what He is saying to us. Explain how you balance feelings and facts when it comes to your faith.

_____

_____

_____

_____

_____

_____

■ Dr. Seamands reminds us of the importance of seeking truth before resting in our feelings. Name some specific ways in which you seek truth in your life.

_____

_____

_____

_____

_____

■ Think of an instance when your feelings led you to the wrong conclusion. Explain how you might have transcended your feelings by talking to yourself in a mature, reasonable way. What might your "self-talk" have sounded like?

_____

_____

_____

_____

_____

_____

_____

Many people depend on feelings as the basis for Christian guidance. One of the great promises of the Christian life is: "For all who are being led by the Spirit of God, these are the sons of God" (Romans 8:14). Nothing is more vital in life than the fact of God's guidance. But many of us misunderstand this to mean that God always leads us by direct feelings and inner impressions. A common phrase now for guidance is "the hot line to heaven" which means a strong, inner emotional push which may be quite independent of outer influences. Some Christians go to ridiculous lengths on these things, even to the point of praying about what stamp to buy at the post office. I hear of college students who pray about whether they should go to a certain campus activity and then about whether they ought to take a date to the event. I don't know whose prayers are getting answered because a lot of the girls sitting alone in the dorm are praying that the boys will have enough sense to date them. There is obviously a clash of prayers here.

This perpetual praying for a feeling or an inner voice on what to do runs all the way from the smallest daily decision to the most serious matters of life. Now the error occurs not about the fact that God does indeed speak through the subjective inner voice, through feelings and impressions. I have had experiences when God did speak that way. The error lies in making feelings and impressions the main source of God's guidance, unchecked and unbalanced with the other, more regular ways in which God guides us.

Feelings and impressions come from three sources: from God, from the devil, and from the inner workings of our minds—our personality patterns, temperament and disposition, emotional hangups and scars, from the damaged emotions of our lives. These are a third source that can be used by either the Holy Spirit or Satan. This is why John warns us, "Beloved, do not believe every spirit, but test the spirits to see whether they are of God" (1 John 4:1, RSV).

A young lady was driving along a country road when she was seized with a strong impression, an overwhelming impulse, that she was to go back and find someone she had passed on the road and witness to him. She was so troubled about it that she came to me for advice. I strongly advised against it; it was obvious to me that there were deep emotional factors in her that Satan was using, not to guide but to misguide. She didn't take the advice but went anyhow. It is a long story and is filled with incidents both ridiculous and dangerous. All that she accomplished was to bring a bad name on the Lord and on the Christian school where she was a student.

The Apostle John's warning means that every subjective Christian experience must be examined and evaluated. It is your moral and spiritual responsibility to test the spirits before you dare to say, "The Lord told me to do this," or, "The Lord led me to do that."

Let me say a couple of things about the matter of guidance. In the everyday decisions of life, you do not need to seek special guidance from God. Many people quote Isaiah 30:21 as the basis for this kind of specific guidance for the daily details of life. "And our ears will hear a word behind you, 'This is the way, walk in it.'" But by failing to quote the rest of the verse they really misquote it and distort its true meaning. The complete verse goes on to say, "Whenever you turn to the right or to the left." In other words, it is only when you start to turn either to the right or to the left and thus start to get off the track that you will hear the voice saying, "This is the way, walk ye in it." As long as you are walking in the right path, obeying the directions of the Lord, you may not hear any special voice of guidance, because you do not need it.

If you are a child of God, the Holy Spirit lives in you, you have surrendered your life to Him, you have given Him the controls—then live! Live self-forgetfully, joyously, freely. Live on the assumption that what you are doing is right, because you have power steering: you are led by the Spirit. To stop and expect some feelings or impression on every simple detail of daily life is a vote of no confidence in the Holy Spirit who indwells you and leads you. It is also unnecessary, and one of the surest ways to drive yourself and everybody around you crazy.

In special times of decision when you need a more specific word from God, remember that guidance is cumulative. Guidance comes through

- ❏ God's Word,
- ❏ outer circumstances (open and closed doors),
- ❏ your own best reasonable thinking,
- ❏ the counsel of other Christians,
- ❏ the inner voice of your feelings.

These are like five great lights God gives us for guidance. No good ship's captain would just go by one light in the channel. He would crash his ship on the rocks or wreck it on a sandbar. Not even two lights or three lights. The trained navigator lines up all of the lights, and then knows he is in the clear, deep channel, and that he can sail safely to his destination.

I remember talking with a missionary pilot just after he had completed a long and difficult course to get his license for instrument flying. After he told me about it, one idea stuck in my mind. He said, "You now, instrument flying is so different from ordinary flying by sight, because you have to learn that you just can't fly by your perception. Sometimes you have to go against your feelings. You just keep your eyes on those instruments. Sometimes you feel as if you are going opposite of what the instruments tell you. You sure can't fly by your feelings."

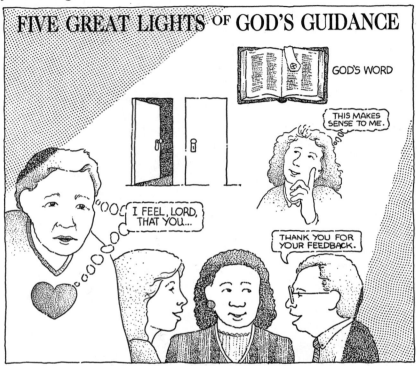

And you can't fly the Christian flight by your feelings either. Keep your eyes on the instruments: God's Word, the pattern of thinking, the outworking of circumstances, and your inner feelings. As much as possible, balance them all together. Put off that childish over-dependency on feelings and impressions as the basis for guidance.

PERSONAL
REFLECTION

■ How do you determine God's guidance in basic decisions you make—not just the small decisions, but the big ones?

_____

_____

_____

_____

■ Describe one of the most difficult decisions you've ever had to make. What steps did you take to determine God's will for you in relationship to that decision? What was the outcome of the decision you made?

_____

_____

_____

_____

_____

■ How much stock do you put in intuition and common sense when seeking God's guidance? How do these three components work together?

_____

_____

_____

■ Can you recall a time when you made an important decision based primarily on your perception and feelings? What was the outcome?

_____

_____

_____

_____

Some people depend on feelings as their motivation for doing good works. John Wesley preached a devastating sermon in which he warned against "the sin of waiting to feel good before you do good."

How often we say, "Well, I just didn't feel like doing it." James wrote, "Whoever knows what is right to do and fails to do it, for him it is sin" (James 4:17, RSV). He did not say, "Whoever knows and feels like doing it." Like little kids we so often wait on feelings as the basis of our motivation—"Well, I did it because I felt like it." Or, "I didn't do it because I just didn't feel like it." In a world like we live in today—where on every hand we hear and see Jesus Christ in dire need, when we can see Christ poor and naked and hungry and imprisoned—we don't need to feel some special kind of urge to Christian service and good works.

Paul told the Ephesian Christians that they were not saved by their good works. We love to quote that part, but we need to go just a little further where he said they were saved unto good works (2:8-10). There are so many unhappy, self-centered Christians who could go a long way toward solving their problems and growing up, if they would quit sitting around taking their spiritual temperature, feeling their emotional pulse, and waiting for some good inner feeling to push them out into the stream of God's service.

To wait to feel good before you do good works is a sin. You can begin now to do some of the good works and services that you know need to be done.

## PERSONAL REFLECTION

■ In his book *My Utmost for His Highest* (Dodd, Mead & Co., p. 116), Oswald Chambers writes: "If we do only what we feel inclined to do some of us would do nothing for ever and ever. There are unemployables in the spiritual domain, spiritual decrepit people, who refuse to do anything unless they are inspired. The proof that we are rightly related to God is that we do our best whether we feel inspired to or not." Does this description fit you in any way? Explain how it does or doesn't.

_____

_____

_____

_____

■ The Apostle Paul says we are not saved *"by* our good works" but *"unto* good works." What idea do you think he's trying to get across to us when he says we are saved "unto good works"?

_____

_____

_____

_____

_____

- Some Christians can't say no when pleas for help are made from the pulpit. The question persists: how does one balance out "doing good works" because one feels called to serve God in a particular way, with doing it just because the need exists or the person feels obligated to do it? How have you learned to balance out these two—duty and choice—in your life?

_____

_____

_____

_____

_____

## PRAYERFUL REFLECTION

- In which of the three feeling areas talked about in this chapter—assurance of salvation, God's guidance, good works—do you need the most help? Write a prayer, expressing to God what you think you need in relationship to that feeling area.

*Dear God,*

_____

_____

_____

_____

_____

_____

_____

_____

## PERSONAL RENEWAL

■ As members of the body of Christ, God's plan for us individually is that we would "grow up in every way into Christ." Set your eye on that goal this week as you read and reflect on Ephesians 4:13-15 (NCV).

*This work must continue until we are all joined together in the same faith and in the same knowledge of the Son of God. We must become like a mature person, growing until we become like Christ and have His perfection. Then we will no longer be babies. We will not be tossed about like a ship that the waves carry one way and then another. We will not be influenced by every new teaching we hear from people who are trying to fool us. They make plans and try any kind of trick to fool people into following the wrong path. No! Speaking the truth with love, we will grow up in every way into Christ, who is the head.*

*I have been crucified with Christ; and it is no longer I who live, but Christ lives in me; and the life which I now live in the flesh I live by faith in the Son of God, who loved me and delivered Himself up for me.*

*Galatians 2:20*


*Do you not know that your body is a temple of the Holy Spirit who is in you, whom you have from God, and that you are not your own? For you have been bought with a price; therefore glorify God in your body.*

*1 Corinthians 6:19-20*

# Chapter 10
# Childish Concepts of Self and Self-Surrender

What does the Bible mean by the word *self*? What do we mean by self-surrender, or complete consecration, crucifixion of the self, death to self, putting self on the cross and Christ on the Throne? These are terms we toss about. Yet our understanding of these concepts is central to the Christian life. If there is cloudiness and confusion, if our minds are filled with immature or sub-Christian ideas, a lot of wrong thinking, wrong feeling, and wrong living are sure to follow.

Dag Hammarskjold was perhaps the most famous Secretary General in the history of the United Nations. When his plane went down in Africa it was such a mystery and for awhile was thought to be sabotage. He was killed in an open field on a clear night. No one could figure out why it happened until the map the pilot was going by was found in the wreckage of the plane. The pilot had the map open to the city of Ndolo which is a town in Zaire. But Hammarskjold intended to go to the city of Ndola which is in Zambia. The pilot crashed thinking he had 1,000 feet more to go on the runway. One letter made the difference between life and death. If you have the wrong mental map of self and of self-surrender, your Christian life will surely end in despair and disillusionment. No concept is more important to a mature understanding of what Christ is asking from you.

Let's think together about some false and harmful ideas of self and self-surrender, to see if we need to put these away.

■ What first comes to mind when you see or hear the term "self-surrender"? Is the idea of surrendering your life to God an appealing one to you? Why?

_____

_____

_____

_____

As a very zealous, youthful Christian I loved the passage in Galatians that says, "I am crucified with Christ." Oh, I liked that! "It is no longer I who live, but Christ, who lives in me." I loved that too. But I did not like the little phrase in-between: "Nevertheless I live" (Galatians 2:20). I didn't consider the phrase quite spiritual enough, until I got to India as a missionary. Then I realized that those three words are most inspired. You see, the Far East tries to solve the problem of the self by getting rid of it. Buddhism says, "Snuff out the candle of self: Nirvana." Hinduism goes at it a little more gently: not self-extinction, but self-absorption into God. The personal, individual selfhood is to be so united with God that it is like a raindrop falling back into the ocean from whence it came, losing its own identity.

"I am crucified with Christ," said Paul, "but I'm still alive. I haven't been destroyed or absorbed or dissolved. I haven't been wiped out." The highest point in the scheme of salvation is when we reach heaven to enjoy fellowship with God throughout eternity. The Christian faith does not have the slightest hint in it that your selfhood or mine will be extinguished when we get there. Forever fix in your mind that your ego comes from God Himself and that selfhood is eternal, imperishable, and indestructible. God does not desire to destroy it. He can fellowship with it and reward it in a heaven; He can isolate it and separate Himself from it in a hell. But it persists. St. Bernard was right when he wrote concerning this essential personhood, "It cannot be burned out, even in hell."

Be careful of falling into error or confusion about self-surrender. "God, take self out of me. God, I want to get to the place where I never think of myself." Such praying is not Christian at all and will mess up your life. This is especially important for young people who are going through the agonies and confusions characteristic of teen years. Adolescence is the age when you are all legs and arms, and falling all over yourself. You are like the centipede who in trying to figure out which leg to put in front of the other one, went down in a heap. You are self-conscious, and in your desperation you cry out for consecration and spirituality which will somehow remove from you the intense consciousness of your existence.

Listen, teenager—if God answers that prayer, you are going to be in bad shape! They will call the ambulance because you'll be in a coma. Even at the height of spirituality you never lose the human gift of self-consciousness.

## PERSONAL REFLECTION

■ In what ways did the family system you grew up in teach you to get rid of your "self"?

_____

_____

_____

_____

_____

■ What about the religious system in which you grew up—what did you learn in it about "self" as it relates to being a truly "spiritual" person?

_____

_____

_____

_____

■ Do you feel like you've abandoned your "self" for one reason or another? How present and alive is your sense of self today?

_____

_____

_____

_____

There are Christians who equate self-denial with self-disparagement. They do this because they do not understand the proper place of self-love in the Christian life. They reject self-love because they see it as the very essence of sin. It is dangerous to think of self as something detached and essentially evil.

Jesus said that we should love God with our whole hearts and love our neighbor as we love ourselves. Love for self is as necessary for maturity and wholeness and holiness as is love for God and for other people. Indeed, loving God and loving my neighbor requires a measure of self-acceptance and self-love in which I hold my own selfhood in esteem, integrity, identity, and respect.

In the great marriage passage of Ephesians, we read that the measure of a man's love for his wife is his love for himself (5:28-29). Commenting on this chapter, John Wesley wrote: "Self-love is not a sin; it is an indisputable duty." Selfishness is a sin, as is self-centeredness, for these are distortions and perversions of love. Never fall into the trap of thinking that crucifixion of the self, self-denial, or self-surrender mean self-contempt or self-despising. Even the word *selflessness* is very misleading. The opposite of pride and self-centeredness is not selflessness or self-contempt, but God-centeredness. "I live, yet not I." Yes, my ego is still alive, but it is not a self-centered, self-filled ego. It is a Christ-filled, Christ-centered ego. Don't make self-belittling or selflessness the goal of your Christian life.

## PERSONAL REFLECTION

■ Do you understand the difference between "self-love," "selfishness," and "self-centeredness"? How might these three concepts display themselves in your life? Write down two or three descriptive phrases that would demonstrate each concept.

**Self-love.** I would _____

_____

_____

_____

**Selfishness.** I would _____

_____

_____

**Self-centeredness.** I would _____

_____

St. Augustine said many wonderful things, but he also made some horrendous blunders. It has taken us centuries to get over some of his extremities regarding the body and sex and self. One of those blunders is in *The City of God:* "The difference between the city of the world and the city of God is that the one is characterized by love of self to the contempt of God, and the other (the city of God) is characterized by love of God to the contempt of self." This is very wrong, very unbiblical, and the way many of us live. We think we are pleasing God. We think we are producing the sanctified and holy life through this kind of counterfeit holiness. In reality, we produce a guilt-ridden piety, a joyless self-negation, an unattractive goodness. Instead of delivering us from self-centeredness and pride, self-contempt leads us into a religious self-centeredness and pride.

In his famous letters to Wormwood, that abominable genius Screwtape gives some subtle advice on the matter. Wormwood is on his first assignment. He always refers to the young Christian he is tempting as the patient. Screwtape writes to Wormwood, "You must therefore conceal from the patient the true end of humility. Let him think of it not as self-forgetfulness but as a certain kind of opinion (namely, a low opinion) of his own talents and character" *(The Screwtape Letters,* C.S. Lewis, Macmillan, p. 72).

Another time when Wormwood has tried all forms of temptation and the young Christian is not falling for any of them, Screwtape writes him, "Your patient has become humble; have you drawn his attention to the fact?" (p. 71)

Self-despising is not pleasing to God, and it is not the answer to the problem of pride. It actually increases the problem. Psychologist Karen Horney has said, "Self-hate is pride's inseparable companion, and you can't have one without the other." How often self-incrimination becomes an inverted form of good works, of inner penance which we must do, thinking we are pleasing to God. It is a badge of membership in an elite holy club which prides itself for self-belittling and guilt. So an amazing thing happens: condemnation of self becomes the basis of "a good conscience."

Some of us wouldn't know how to live if we didn't feel guilty; we'd go to pieces from spiritual anxiety. That guilty self becomes the basis of a "good conscience," while a good conscience somehow creates a feeling of guilt. It reminds me of a cartoon I saw. Two convicts in a prison courtyard are whispering about a third. The first convict says to the second, "You know, the thing I can't stand about that guy is his guiltier-than-thou attitude."

"Love your neighbor as you love yourself," said Jesus. Self-love, not selflessness, is the basis of interpersonal relationships. Selflessness between people can turn out to be mere compliance and appeasement. It is often used to rationalize copping-out on the tough, real-life questions of right and wrong. And, of course, selflessness in the hands of a Christian bully can become an exquisite instrument of torture, of spiritual and emotional blackmail. If he can make you feel guilty by saying to you, "You're thinking about yourself," then he can control and manipulate you into doing whatever he wants.

The heart of the Christian life is love—loving God with the whole self and loving others as you love yourself. Don't translate that "Love your neighbor instead of yourself." "Love your neighbor as you love yourself," Jesus said. This requires not less of a self, but more of a self filled with power and love.

## PERSONAL REFLECTION

■ What does "counterfeit holiness" look like? Are you guilty of living this way?

_____

_____

_____

_____

■ The Apostle Paul challenged the believers at Philippi with these words, "Don't be selfish; don't live to make a good impression on others. Be humble, thinking of others as better than yourself" (Philippians 2:3, TLB). What do you think he was saying? What have religious teachers taught you that this verse means?

_____

_____

_____

_____

■ What is the "true end" of humility? What does a truly humble person look like?

_____

_____

_____

_____

■ Do you love yourself? Why or why not? Describe behaviors you exhibit that demonstrate healthy self-love.

_____

_____

_____

_____

Another inadequate answer to self which has come about in recent years through a veritable explosion of OKness psychology is self-actualization. It says, "Accept yourself, express yourself." In this school of psychology, the self does not need to be surrendered, only developed. Perhaps one of the reasons for this solution is that we Christians went to an extreme with our self-despising. While it contains much that is true and helpful, it is not a biblical answer to the problem of self. Alan Reuter, a Lutheran counselor, has written an interesting book, _Who Says I'm OK?_ (Concordia). While Reuter expresses appreciation of the OKness psychology, he reveals its inadequacies and shows how it can become another false god on the market, another means for escaping the true selfhood that God wants. This approach leaves self at the center of your life. It feeds the very disease it is trying to cure, that is, a self which is independent of God and sufficient without Him. It promotes personhood centered not on God, but on self. Such worship of a false god—whether done in a pagan way or in a relatively religious way—does not answer the problem of the self. It may only pamper our childish self-centeredness and keep us from true maturity in Christ.

PERSONAL
REFLECTION

■ Two concepts being perpetuated by popular personal growth experts today tell us to develop our "personal potential" and to tap into our "personal power"? In what ways, if any, have you bought into this "self-actualizing" system of thinking?

_____

_____

_____

_____

_____

_____

■ Self-actualization leaves "self" at the center of our lives. . . . A self which is independent of God and sufficient without Him. Why do you think this concept leads us *away from* rather than *toward* self-surrender?

_____

_____

_____

_____

Any false and immature understanding of the self and self-surrender leaves the person self-sufficient, self-righteous, self-willed, seeking his own glory. In a word, basically unsurrendered. Many a Christian accepts God's sovereignty in every other realm of life except over his inner self. This is often so subtle that only the Holy Spirit can reveal the error. Such a person may be willing to work for God, to pray and to witness. Yes, and even to preach with the tongues of men and angels, to move mountains by faith, to give everything to feed the poor, and even to give his body to be burned and to die as a Christian martyr. The unsurrendered self will go to great lengths to prevent its dethronement. It will rise to heights of sacrificial service. I have seen missionaries travel thousands of miles, crossing many oceans, who fail to take the last step required for self-surrender. That last step is to the cross of Jesus Christ. It was there, says Paul, that when Christ died we were united with Him in the likeness of His death . . . for our old self was crucified with Him (Romans 6:5-6). We will be looking at this more specifically in the next chapter.

It is only when I surrender myself to God, when I allow Him to take center stage of my life, when I put myself under His authority, when I am filled with His love, that I can love Him with my whole self. Only then do I possess the true self-esteem and self-love that enables me to love other people. You cannot reverse these two and come out right. Then the true self can be cultivated, accepted, realized, actualized, and developed to its fullest potential. When God is truly God, then I can truly be who I am. "I've gotta be me," says the song. Sure! But I can't be me until He is truly He. When God is at the center of my life, then I can like the me I am, because my self is on-center.

I have to laugh at the philosophers and the psychologists who say that the Christian concept of self-surrender destroys the self, inhibits our manhood or womanhood, prevents self-development, and keeps people from being at their best. The lower I kneel at the feet of Jesus Christ, the taller I stand in my own unique selfhood. Chained to Christ as His bondservant, I become free and for the first time can like who I am. The self is released from trying to be someone it isn't and was never intended to be. As a result you and I can become what we were meant to be.

"Nevertheless I live," says Paul, "yet it is not I." I'm not destroyed, I'm not extinguished. I'm alive, yes, but better still, Christ now lives in me and the life I live is really His life being lived in me and through me. And now I can say, "Sure, I'm OK, and you're OK."

Many Christians feel that self-surrender will destroy them. Why do they think this? Because of false, immature, and even unchristian ideas of what self-surrender is, ideas which bring fear and hesitation, which keep them from that which gives the greatest joy and fulfillment of life—total surrender to Christ.

One night I preached a sermon entitled, "Unconditional Surrender," and the Holy Spirit gripped the heart of a young man named Ed. He came to the counseling room that week and said, "Doc, that is what I need to do, but I'm afraid." Now Ed was quite an athlete and especially talented in gymnastics. I will never forget his illustration. He said, "I need to surrender; I want to, but I'm afraid. I'll tell you how it feels. It's like I am over in the gym and grab hold of the bar. I'm ready to work out on it when all of a sudden they pull the bar up until it is almost to the ceiling. Way up high, I'm just hanging on for dear life. And the Holy Spirit says to me, 'Ed, let go . . . Surrender . . . Let go, Ed.' But I'm so far up that when I look down there are clouds below me. And Doc, I can't see where I am going to land." He looked me straight in the eye and continued, "All I ask is that God show me where I am going to land."

I replied, "Ed, that's the catch. Real self-surrender is when you give up your right to yourself. That means you give up the right to ask where you will land. But Ed, you have nothing to worry about because you will land in the arms of love."

But Ed was afraid and hesitant. Though we met and prayed several times, he never really let go. He graduated and I didn't see him for several years. Then one fall during the Homecoming weekend Ed came back to Wilmore. On Sunday morning the church was filled with guests. After the service I went to the back of the church where a long line of alumni wanted to greet their former pastor. They were quickly passing by me when suddenly I recognized Ed. His face was glowing, radiant. He came and shook my hand so warmly and said, "Doc, I just want to tell you one thing: I let go, I let go." He had found out that he didn't need to be afraid. He could let go because he would land in the arms of Perfect Love. And so will you.

## PERSONAL REFLECTION

■ In his book *Hunger for Healing*, Keith Miller says, "For many thousands of people, the Twelve Steps of Alcoholics Anonymous have become the spiritual discipline for a new decade, a way to turn to God and begin a pilgrimage toward wholeness. Step Three focuses on surrendering your will and life over to the care of God. But this idea of surrendering, of releasing authority and control of outcomes to another, is a very difficult notion for thinking people." (Harper-Collins, p. 47) What do you feel when you consider really putting your life and your will—your whole future—in God's hands?

_____

_____

_____

_____

_____

■ What are the specific fears that come to mind when you consider turning all of your life over to the care of God? Are there any areas in particular that you resist turning over? Why?

_____

_____

_____

_____

■ It is nearly impossible to surrender to someone we don't wholeheartedly trust. Can you think of areas in which you do not trust God (e.g., finances, family matters, intimacy needs)? List them below.

_____

_____

_____

_____

_____

_____

■ Can you see the roots of any of these areas of fear and lack of trust in God in your childhood relationships with your parents? Describe them.

_____

_____

_____

_____

_____

## PRAYERFUL REFLECTION

■ Dr. Seamands concludes chapter 10 with this prayer:

*Dear God,*
*We rebuke Screwtape and all of his emissaries for filling our minds with fearful ideas. They tell us that if we really let You take over, You will destroy us, hurt us. O God, rebuke the powers of evil that so many of us struggle with, and help Your children to find the joy and fulfillment of the Christ-centered self. Answer our deepest prayers. In Jesus' name we pray. Amen.*

■ If you have already committed your heart and life to Jesus Christ, are you ready now to put your life and your will in His hands—to trust Him completely to do what is in your best interest even when you may feel otherwise? If you are ready, then write out your own commitment prayer letting God know of your readiness.

_____

_____

_____

_____

_____

_____

_____

## PERSONAL RENEWAL

■ Are you convinced at a heartfelt level that God truly does have your best interest at heart? Shore up your confidence in the God who loves you by reflecting on this description of him found in Psalm 145:8-9, 17-20 (TLB).

*Jehovah is kind and merciful, slow to get angry, full of love. He is good to everyone, and His compassion is intertwined with everything He does. . . . The LORD is fair in everything He does and full of kindness. He is close to all who call on Him sincerely. He fulfills the desires of those who reverence and trust Him; He hears their cries for help and rescues them. He protects all those who love Him, but destroys the wicked.*

*For if we have become united with Him in the likeness of His death, certainly we shall be also in the likeness of His resurrection, knowing this, that our old self was crucified with Him, that our body of sin might be done away with, that we should no longer be slaves to sin; for he who has died is freed from sin.*

*Now if we have died with Christ, we believe that we shall also live with Him, knowing that Christ, having been raised from the dead, is never to die again; death no longer is master over Him. For the death that He died, He died to sin, once for all; but the life that He lives, He lives to God.*

*Even so consider yourselves to be dead to sin, but alive to God in Christ Jesus.*

*Romans 6:5-11*

# Chapter 11
# The Ultimate Crisis of Life

The word *ultimate* means something beyond which there is nothing more important or decisive. Self-surrender is the ultimate crisis of human life.

Self-surrender is the ultimate crisis because it represents the ultimate spiritual battle. Everything else in the Christian experience is a preamble to this. Everything else is the work of the Holy Spirit in prevenient and wooing grace, paving the way for this great divine/human encounter.

Self-surrender begins in our inheritance, in the home with all of its influences, in the conviction of our sins, the agony of struggling with guilt, the painful attempt to win God's approval by trying to do better and be better by lopping off this sin and that sin, and even in the putting on of religious disciplines. Then comes the realization that we are dependent completely upon grace. Next is the joyous discovery that we don't have to do our moral housecleaning before we come to God, but can come as we are, receive His full and free and absolute forgiveness, and know the joyous experience of conversion, of becoming a new creation.

This is followed by growth in grace, the ups and downs of Christians who, having begun in the Spirit, fall back into the way of the law. Then the desperate attempt to please God, to be all that we think He wants us to be, often with the mistaken notion that following and obeying a holy law can make us holy. And all along, at every step of the way, the Holy Spirit is working with us on the emotional hang-ups we have been talking about, helping us to put away childish things and grow more and more mature.

All of these important steps are the growing pains through which God "leads His dear children along," until we finally see what the real challenge is. Everything up to this point has been a minor skirmish in comparison to the ultimate battle to which we are being led lovingly, ruthlessly, relentlessly, wooingly, but oh, so firmly. We are being taken by the Holy Spirit to the place where we see that the real issue is the surrender of self to the lordship of Jesus Christ. As the Holy Spirit leads us, sometimes gently, sometimes rather roughly, but always lovingly, suddenly the surroundings look familiar. For we see that He has brought us to a spot we recognize, a skull-shaped hill we call Calvary. It is at the cross that the crucifixion of the self-centeredness of my ego is going to take place. And this is the greatest battle of every life.

## PERSONAL REFLECTION

■ Dr. Seamands writes, "Self-surrender is the ultimate crisis because it represents the ultimate spiritual battle." Try to imagine a battlefield—a spiritual battlefield. You are standing at one side of the field facing the enemy and are about to engage in combat. Now picture in your mind's eye the enemies of your soul (i.e., those things in your life that seem to keep you self-defeated or from experiencing the reality of God and the personal presence of Jesus Christ at the innermost part of your being). Maybe it's a quick temper, or compulsive worrying, or deep-rooted shame. Or it might be the resentments of fractured relationships, broken dreams, cycles of depression, or insatiable lust. Every one of us wars against something. Once you have conjured up an image of your own spiritual battlefield, try to capture it in picture form. You may choose to use a page of the *Personal Journal* section in Appendix Three of this workbook, or use a sheet of your own drawing paper if you think you need more space. Crayons or colored markers can add a sense of emotion or intensity to what you envision the enemy to be. Give this exercise both time and thought!

Jesus made it clear that anyone who does not renounce all that he has cannot be His disciple: "Whoever does not bear his own cross and come after Me, cannot be My disciple" (Luke 14:2, RSV). The words I want you to notice especially are: "Come after Me." I believe this is a far deeper call to commitment and surrender than Jesus' first call, "Come unto Me."

"Come unto Me" is the first step. But it is after disciples come to Jesus that He begins to make things harder for them. Some leaders say to their followers, "I'm going to ask very little of you." Jesus never says that. He tells us to count the cost. He makes His demands more stringent; He ups the price; He winnows and sifts out those who follow Him. He seems afraid of having too many, so He thins out the ranks. He separates the dabblers from the disciples.

The Holy Spirit takes us through this process of self-exposure so that we will see what the real issue is. For our basic sin lies much deeper than the daily sins which are its outward form, deeper than the infirmities and hang-ups which, though not sinful in themselves, do predispose us to certain sins. The real sin is the unsurrenderedness of the ego. This sin is the root; the sins are the fruit.

It is so subtle, so undiscernible to the naked eye that only the Holy Spirit—through this process and through the Word of God, which is the sharp, two-edged sword, piercing to the innermost depths—can bring us to the place where we see the ultimate battle, namely the need for the crucifixion, the death of self-centeredness.

"I am crucified with Christ: nevertheless I live; yet not I, but Christ liveth in me." Galatians 2:20 is the most self-surrendered verse in the New Testament. But strangely enough, it is also the most self-filled verse in the New Testament. Did you know that there are eight personal pronouns in that one little testimony? "I"— five times. "Me"—three times. It is self-filled and self-surrendered at the same time. Confusing? A contradiction? No, it's the great paradox at the very heart of the Christian life and must be understood if we are to go on to real maturity. We need to identify the three facets of the ego. The difficulty is that we use the personal pronoun "I" to cover all three of the facets.

"I have been crucified with Christ"—that is one facet of the ego. It needs the death dealing effects of crucifixion.

"Nevertheless I live"—that is obviously another facet of the ego. It is the selfhood which survives self-crucifixion, a selfhood which is indestructible and eternal. Christ is not at all interested in crucifying or destroying it; He is only interested in liberating it and in developing it to its fullest and highest. This indestructible, imperishable ego will be alive, either in heaven or hell, a billion years from now, and God Himself cannot destroy it. He wanted it for His eternal fellowship!

"Yet," says Paul, "not I, but Christ lives in me." That's the answer: the Christ-filled, the Christ-possessed, Christ-centered ego.

The first facet of the ego is the one which is fallen, diseased, perverted, and twisted. It always turns in on itself and raises its will. It prevents my true self from reaching its highest potential and being what God planned for it to be. This facet of the ego with its malignant self-centeredness and self-sufficiency, needs to die. We talk about Custer's last stand, which was a bloody battle. The crucifixion of self is everyone's last stand because it is the ultimate battle.

It may take a long time to travel from conversion to self-surrender. One of the mistakes in our philosophy of holiness and sanctification is to ask people to do something that is psychologically and emotionally impossible: namely, to move too quickly from conversion to self-surrender. It seems that God has to bring most of us through a series of steps until we arrive at total desperation. And only God can do that for us. No preacher, no amount of emotional manipulation can do this. There is a temptation to subject new Christians to spiritual pressure until they say, "Yes, it's done." But by so doing, we turn them into spiritual phonies. Some people have been so badly damaged they need healing before there is a real self to surrender. Not everyone is ready for the message of self-surrender at the same time. We need to leave people in the hands of the Spirit who prepares them for the ultimate crisis.

## PERSONAL REFLECTIONS

■ Are you clear in your own thinking about the three different facets of the ego Dr. Seamands describes above: (1) the self-centered, "I-am-in-control-of-my-own-life" ego; (2) the God-created, indestructible, eternal self—the real me—ego; (3) the Christ-filled, Christ-centered ego? What questions, if any, do you have concerning what it means to surrender your SELF to God? Jot your questions down here.

_____

_____

_____

_____

■ In his book *Hunger for Healing,* author Keith Miller talks about sin in this way:

At an existential, everyday level of thinking, sin is thought to refer to "bad things one does" such as theft, adultery, murder, gossiping, judging, and so forth. But as William Temple pointed out, these things are only symptoms of a deeper disease. He says there is only one Sin (with a capital S), and that is putting ourselves in the center of our lives and other people's lives, where only God should be. Sins with a small s are those specific things we do as a result of putting ourselves in the center (like stealing, adultery, and trying to control people (HarperCollins, p. 3).

Are you guilty of Sin (with a capital S)? Describe why you see yourself as being guilty of Sin. What kinds of sin (with a small s) seem to be part of your life most frequently?

_____

_____

■ In recovery circles today, you are likely to hear people talk about "giving up control" rather than "surrendering one's self." These two concepts are one and the same—at the heart of each phrase is the matter of learning to "let go and let God." Though it may sound trite, letting go and letting God be Lord in our lives is a very difficult thing to do. Who is in control of your life right now? To what or whom have you given permission to be the god of your life at this present moment?

_____

_____

_____

■ God alone knows when our hearts are truly ready to surrender to Him as Lord of our lives. Have you ever tried to "give God a hand" in the life of a friend or family member by pushing that person toward becoming "self-surrendered" before he or she was ready? What happened? Has anyone ever pushed you toward self-surrender before you were ready? How did you feel about that?

_____

_____

_____

It took me four years to get from "here to there." In the battlefield of my spiritual life where the Holy Spirit led me deeper and deeper, I surrendered many attachments, many relationships, many ambitions. I was healed of many hang-ups and damaged emotions. I answered the call to preach and to go to the mission field. But I hung on to myself until the Spirit in His gracious work, largely through the reading of Oswald Chambers' book *My Utmost for His Highest*, took the veil from my eyes. One lonely summer, as a student at Asbury College I saw it, but I didn't realize what had happened until three weeks later. So don't give me that stuff about "if it happens to you, you'll always know it at the time." That isn't so. There are a lot of things on the market that just ain't so! I got in through the back window and didn't know it. But one miserable July night on the third floor of Morrison dormitory, I saw my self as I never had before: I saw all of its loathsomeness, its deceptiveness, its rebelliousness.

You see, before my conversion I felt convicted as a guilty criminal who had broken God's laws. But now I felt a different conviction. It was not that I was breaking God's laws. Rather, it was as if I were guilty of treason against the state, that I had within me an unyielded being that questioned the very right and rulership of God Himself. One statement of Chambers kept hammering at my heart: "Total surrender is when you give up your right to yourself." Isn't it amazing! Oswald Chambers said that a quarter of a century before J.B. Phillips translated the New Testament and rendered Jesus' command in Mark 8:34 like this: "If anyone wants to follow in My footsteps, he must give up all right to himself, take up his cross and follow Me."

Surrender is the ultimate crisis because it is the ultimate battle. There are many images that may help you at this point. You may picture your heart as a house with many rooms. This is an act whereby you turn over to Christ, room by room, every portion of your personality, particularly the control room, the throne room, the ruling room. Or you may picture the various areas of your life where you need to surrender to God's will—your plans, ambitions, sex life, romance, marriage, leisure, and choice of a life's vocation.

Or picture your own image of who you are, and what you think other people think about you, your name, your work, and your spiritual reputation. I believe that was the crux of my battle. You see, I wanted people to think I was "spiritual." I wasn't particularly interested in worldly things, so they weren't hard to give up. But I did want people to think I was spiritual, and that was a hard battle. I had to take my spiritual reputation and hand it over to Christ.

What was the first step in the *kenosis*, the self-emptying and the self-surrender of Jesus? He, "who being in the form of God thought it not robbery to be equal with God but made Himself of no reputation" (Philippians 2:6-7). He emptied Himself. That was the first step. Have you ever given your spiritual reputation over to Christ? We live in such bondage to other people because we want them to think we are spiritual. This leads to neurosis in the Christian life and to introspection and slavery.

Some people mistakenly illustrate self-surrender this way—you take a blank sheet of paper and on it write a long list of things you want. "Lord, give me this, give me that, give me the other." It is like a grocery shopping list. Then you sign your name and hand it over to God saying, "Lord, I surrender. Take my life and let it be."

But that is not what surrender is all about, so let's start over. Take a blank sheet of paper and sign your name at the bottom. Now hand it to God and say, "Lord, You fill it in. And whatever You fill in, my name remains signed at the bottom forever."

**PERSONAL REFLECTION**

■ Oswald Chambers reminds us that "total surrender is when you give up your right to yourself." Is there anything in your life that you feel unable to give up your right to at present? What is it? Describe how you feel about giving it up.

_____

_____

_____

■ What is your greatest source of inner conflict concerning the thing(s) you listed in the previous question? What is your greatest fear in surrendering this part of your life—or who you are—to God?

_____

_____

_____

_____

■ Describe how you feel about the "blank sheet" concept of self-surrender Dr. Seamands mentions above.

_____

_____

_____

Self-surrender is the ultimate crisis because it is the all-inclusive crisis, encompassing all other crises of life. Dr. Henry Clay Morrison used to say in his down-to-earth way, "When you come to the altar for consecration, you are bringing two bundles with you: one bundle is the 'known' of your life, and the other is the 'unknown.' In full consecration you put them both on the altar."

This causes a lot of confusion and anxiety, particularly among young people. Self-surrender is both a definite crisis and a never-ending process. When we talk about self-surrender we are talking about a commitment of your will to the lordship of Christ. Now you can do that at any given time, provided you are ready. If the Holy Spirit has "ripened" you, it is your _kairos_ time. If it is your _kairos_ time, it is God's time.

## PERSONAL REFLECTION

■ Self-surrender is a commitment of your will to the lordship of Christ. Here again we are reminded of the words of Step Three of Alcoholics Anonymous' Twelve Steps: "[We] made a decision to turn our will and our lives over to the care of God as we understood Him." Turning our lives over means consciously relinquishing our destructive self-will and our compulsive behaviors, as well as our talents, potentials, skills, ambitions, and relationships to God. This is a never ending process. Many of us are willing to surrender the "problem" areas of our lives to God because we see how unmanageable they make our lives. However, there are other parts of our lives that we tend to cling to because we think we can still manage them. What we eventually realize is that we cannot barter with God. We must be prepared to surrender our entire will and every part of our lives to His care. Which parts of your life are you most willing to turn over to God? In which areas of your life do you struggle most with self-will and a stubborn inability to give up?

_____

_____

_____

When you surrender, what are you giving up? Your will. You are surrendering your willingness to Christ, but the content of that will is something that you will fill in from now on throughout your life. Long ago I realized that if I didn't make it very clear, in asking Christians to surrender, I was really asking them to do something that was psychologically impossible, because *you cannot surrender to God something of which you are not aware.* Let me put it positively: you can only surrender to God that which you first acknowledge to yourself. You can surrender your willingness to God, you can make a total surrender of your right to yourself, you can make a full commitment surrender. But you won't actually be surrendering anything specific until you face some particular issue of the will in a real-life situation. And that is the confusing part. You may make a total surrender to the lordship of Christ, and then come to something two weeks later where there will be a struggle between your emotions and your will. Right away Screwtape gets on your shoulder and says, "Ah, hum! You really didn't surrender a couple of weeks ago in church, did you!" And unless we have a mature mind, we will be prone to fall for that deception.

God said to the Children of Israel, "All of Canaan is yours, but you must possess it. It is yours provided you put the soles of your feet upon it" (Joshua 1:3). You may fully surrender your willingness to

God's will, but all that you are doing is renouncing your right to your will. You are saying, "God, I will to choose Your will in every situation in my life." You surrender your right to make your choices on the basis of what you would like, and you commit yourself to find and follow, discover and do God's will. Yes, that is a crisis, but it also has to become a daily process, because we actually surrender concrete things and situations only as they come into our awareness.

When you make this full surrender you are promising, "God, my will is Yours," which is really saying, "Now, God, when anything comes up, I will choose what You choose." But, you see you have not yet surrendered anything, you have not yet actually chosen anything. And when you do come down to actualizing it, you may encounter a struggle between your emotions and the commitment you once made. Complete surrender doesn't computerize you into automatic, robot-like choices.

I don't know of a better illustration of this than Jesus' great struggle in the Garden of Gethsemane. Most people do not take a profound look at that experience. It was a terrific struggle during which Jesus fell on the ground three times in agony. What was the struggle all about? Had not Jesus long ago made a total surrender of His life? Was not Jesus' will in absolute agreement with His Father's will? Of course. Had He not said all of His life, "My food is God's will; My will is God's will; My joy is to do the will of My Father"? Yes, there is no question about the depth of Jesus' total surrender to and alignment with the Father's will. But there was still a profound struggle in the Garden between Jesus' emotions and His will. Every surrendered Christian knows what that means. The most sanctified saint has been through this and may go through it again tomorrow. I find it interesting that Jesus accepted His emotional struggle without any shame! And the New Testament writers make no effort to cover or soften it.

So let's not give young Christians the false idea that surrender is something you do once for all. You may make the commitment of intention once for all. You may say, "Not my will, but Yours be done," and mean it for the rest of your life. But to actualize this, to make it real in concrete situations, is a lifetime process. It is something you get better at as you mature in the Spirit-filled life. All of us would live saner, safer, sweeter, more effective lives if we could honestly admit to ourselves and to God that we, like Jesus, experience a struggle at times between our emotions and our will.

A young lady who came to me for counseling was deeply in love. But she was beginning to realize that, as much as she loved the young man, he was not the right one for her because of some genuine spiritual differences that she saw as insurmountable. So she wrote him a letter, they talked about it, and then she broke it off. Some days later she came to me in tears, depressed, all torn up. What was wrong? Well, she had some well-meaning friends who assured her that there must be something wrong with her spiritually or she wouldn't be having such a struggle. She was crying a lot, couldn't do her work, and wasn't able to concentrate on her studies. She knew she had done the right thing and didn't have the slightest intention of going back on her decision, but her feelings were giving her a rough time. Instead of helping her bear the burden, her well-intentioned but misinformed friends had added a burden of spiritual guilt to her already overburdened heart. I said to her, "Honey, of course you can cry. Of course you are feeling blue. Of course you are struggling. But tell me, what is the direction of your will?" She replied at once, "That hasn't changed, because I know what I must do." We opened the New Testament and read together the story of Christ's struggle in the Garden of Gethsemane. She saw the point. Her commitment to God's will was firm and steady. But her emotions were battered and putting up a struggle. Someone has rightly said, "Your will can go ahead by express, but your emotions sometimes travel by slow freight."

When I am in conflict, the best thing I can do is to take my feelings to God in rigorous honesty and tell Him what they really are. Then I reaffirm the full surrender I made many years ago and apply it to this specific situation.

You can surrender your will. You can make the all-out surrender now if He has readied you for it. This is the great battle, and the great crisis. But it is not the end. Rather, it is an open end, in which you begin a lifetime process of specific surrenders to the Lord.

## PERSONAL REFLECTION

■ Dr. Seamands reminds us that we actually surrender concrete things and situations only as we become consciously aware of them in our lives. Think of a specific situation you are dealing with at present where your emotions and God's will are coming into conflict. Imagine carrying on a conversation with Jesus concerning your struggle. Write out how you think that conversation might go.

_____

_____

_____

_____

■ As we see from the life of Jesus in the Garden of Gethsemane, there is no shame in struggling to bring our emotions and God's will into alignment. Christ, who fully understands the struggle, invites us to take our feelings to God in a rigorously honest way. What, if anything, keeps you from being rigorously honest with God?

_____

_____

_____

Self-surrender is the ultimate crisis because it is the essential secret of life itself. It is the means of finding my true self, of becoming what God planned for me, of discovering my personal uniqueness. Self-surrender is the death which is followed by resurrection. It is a paradox, for if you lose your life, you will save it; but if you try to save it, you will lose it. *The New English Bible* translates Mark 8:34-37 this way: "Anyone who wishes to be a follower of Mine must leave self behind; he must take up his cross, and come with Me. . . . What does a man gain by winning the whole world at the cost of his true self? What can he give to buy that self back?"

We give up our self-centered and twisted selves to find our true selves. The aim of God in self-surrender is not the destruction of self; it is the birth and growth of the true self He intended you to be.

In his book, *How You Can Find Happiness*, Sam Shoemaker gives this testimony:

> I can well remember a time in my life, long after my first deci-
> sive spiritual experience, when I was facing the need to take
> another big step forward. I could almost see my "self" shrinking
> out of sight under the withering effects of an honest facing of
> my faults, and, like Alice in Wonderland when she was shrink-
> ing, I wondered whether I wouldn't go out like a light if this
> process went on! But this was not the real case: when I let go
> deeply inside, my true "self" was never more fulfilled and
> expressed, and I realized that all this fanfare of resistance and
> self-will is the protective device of the ego to keep the true "self"
> from emerging and being victorious. This fear of giving up, of
> giving in, is a contrivance of the ego. As Fenelon said, "If we
> looked carefully into ourselves, we should find some secret
> place where we hide what we think we are not obliged to
> sacrifice to God." But until that false ego dies, the true self
> cannot live. And the death of an ego is the greatest of all human
> crises (Dutton, pp. 91-92).

## PERSONAL REFLECTION

■ Hold on to this truth: *The aim of God in self-surrender is not the destruction of self; it is the birth and growth of the true self He intended you to be.* How much of your true self have you found as the result of surrendering your life to God? Are you really convinced that the more of your *self* you give to God the more of your true *self* He gives back to you? Write a brief testimony stating how God has brought you to a new level of emotional and spiritual maturity as the result of learning to surrender your life to Him a situation at a time.

_____

_____

_____

Self-surrender is the ultimate crisis because it is the answer to life. This self dies in order to truly live. This captive self surrenders not to be destroyed, annihilated, or absorbed, but to be liberated, to be its true and best self. George Matheson's great hymn captures these truths most beautifully.

### Make Me a Captive, Lord
Make me a captive, Lord, and then I shall be free;
Force me to render up my sword, and I shall conqueror be.
I sink in life's alarms when by myself I stand;
Imprison me within Thine arms, and strong shall be my hand.

My heart is weak and poor until it master find;
It has no spring of action sure, it varies with the wind.
It cannot freely move till Thou has wrought its chain;
Enslave it with Thy matchless love, and deathless it shall reign.

My will is not my own till Thou hast made it Thine;
If it would reach a monarch's throne, it must its crown resign;
It only stands unbent, amid the clashing strife,
When on Thy bosom it has leant and found in Thee its life.

                                                Amen.

## PRAYERFUL REFLECTION

■ As you've already seen, self-surrender means giving your will and your life over to Jesus Christ, each day, each moment, just the way that you are. It is synonymous with seeking His presence, guidance, and counsel throughout the day. Surrender leads to peace and serenity. "The Serenity Prayer" best captures the surrender cycle. Read this prayer aloud any time you find your feelings coming in conflict with what you know to be God's will.

### The Serenity Prayer
*God, grant me the serenity
to accept the things I cannot change,*

*the courage to change the things I can,*
*and the wisdom to know the difference.*
*Living one day at a time,*
*enjoying one moment at a time;*
*accepting hardship as a pathway to peace;*
*taking, as Jesus did,*
*this sinful world as it is,*
*not as I would have it;*
*trusting that You will make all things right*
*if I surrender to Your will;*
*so that I may be reasonably happy in this life*
*and supremely happy with You forever in the next.*
*AMEN.*

—Reinhold Niebuhr

## PERSONAL RENEWAL

■ In the Garden of Gethsemane, Jesus demonstrated some qualities that are important for us in recovery: honesty, transparency, and trust. As you read and reflect on Mark 14:32-36 this week, ask God to help you cultivate these same qualities in your own life.

*And now they came to an olive grove called the Garden of Gethsemane, and He instructed His disciples, "Sit here, while I go and pray." He took Peter, James, and John with Him and began to be filled with horror and deepest distress. And He said to them, "My soul is crushed by sorrow to the point of death; stay here and watch with Me." He went on a little further and fell to the ground and prayed that if it were possible the awful hour awaiting Him might never come. "Father, Father," He said, "everything is possible for You. Take away this cup from Me. Yet I want Your will, not Mine."*

*"Behold, I am making all things new."*

*Revelation 21:5*

# Chapter 12
# Reprogramming Grace

In the preceding chapters we have dealt with the many different ways the inner child of the past manifests itself and interferes with our adult lives. We have seen that this growing up procedure requires us to *katargeo* that child in several areas of our lives. There are powerful childhood and teenage memories which need to be healed. There are subtle childish acts of concealment and defense which need to be unmasked. There are unhealthy childish complexes and compulsions that need to be broken. There are unrealistic mottoes whose dictatorial power over us needs to be challenged. There are unruly feelings which need to be saddled, and shackled feelings which need to be freed. There are infantile lies which need to be rebuked, babyish confusions which need to be cleared, and naive concepts which need to be straightened out.

The process requires both negative and positive efforts. As we *katargeo* the negative behaviors, we must be sure that mature, positive feelings, understanding concepts, and actions take their place. That's why this process requires the whole person in every aspect of personality—thought, emotion, will, and behavior. It requires growing up in our personal relationships—with ourselves, others, and God.

PERSONAL
REFLECTION

■ Are you ready to "grow up"? If so, think through your own personal strategy for "putting away childish things" by answering the following series of questions.

■ Are you aware of any powerful memories from the past which still need to be healed? Make a list of them.

_____

_____

_____

_____

_____

_____

■ What, if any, self-defensive masks do you wear to conceal the truth about your real self?

_____

_____

_____

_____

_____

■ Do you struggle with feelings of inferiority in any areas of your life? What are they?

_____

_____

_____

_____

_____

■ Are you compulsive in any way? List your compulsive behaviors.

_____

_____

_____

_____

_____

■ Are you able to feel and express your emotions in a balanced way? Explain. Which feelings are the most difficult for you to express?

_____

_____

_____

_____

_____

■ What childish ideas or mottoes do you continue to hold on to even though they get you in trouble?

_____

_____

_____

_____

_____

Most of us would agree that the greatest problem in our lives is ourselves. As Samuel Hoffenstein put it, "The trouble with me is that everywhere I go, I go too, and that spoils everything!"

A little boy came home from school one day and asked his mother, "Mama, how do wars get started?"

She replied, "Well, if you're talking about the last war, it got started when Germany attacked Belgium."

Dad, who had been buried in the evening newspaper, came up for air and said, "No, Son, it wasn't Belgium; it was when Germany attacked Poland."

But the mother insisted, "No, I'm sure I remember correctly; it was Belgium."

"Now what do you know about it?" corrected the father. "You didn't go to college. I did, and I minored in world history. I tell you the war began when the Germans attacked Poland."

It wasn't very long until the parents were in a heated argument; soon they were shouting at each other. The little boy tugged at his mother and she snapped at him, "Well, what do you want?"

He said, "That's OK, Mama. Now I think I know how wars get started."

From within that hidden child in all of us some incredibly immature behaviors can emerge. So much of what we are is rooted in the early developmental years of our lives. This is not to deny the biblical fact of original sin and the fallenness of our natures. Nor is it to belittle our own sins, in which "we have each turned to our own willful ways" (Isaiah 53:6). But it is to remind us that it is all further complicated by a vast range of childish things which could be classed more as infirmities and cripplings—weaknesses which predispose us toward certain kinds of sins, limitations which make us more liable to certain kinds of temptations.

## PERSONAL REFLECTION

■ In his first book, *Healing for Damaged Emotions*, Dr. Seamands describes the biblical term *infirmities* as "crippling weaknesses that sabotage our happiness and relationships and keep us from taking responsibility for our own lives" (Victor, p. 39). List any "infirmities" which you are aware of in your life.

_____

_____

_____

_____

_____

Some years ago I saw an ad which claimed that a certain lawn food was supposed to help the grass grow thicker and healthier. It said, "The shoots grow down before they grow up, and what they find to root in will determine how they grow up." Our adult lives are deeply rooted in our childhood/teenage years and deeply affected by them. I was fascinated by a magazine article written about a well-known college football player which stressed this:

You could say that we become what we are, not so much in the sanctuary of the womb or the groves of academe, but in that Elysian drive-in joint known as High School. . . . It is there that we are nurtured, our personalities shaped, our bodies structured, our habits and moods and values all having jockeyed for position in the chaotic halls of puberty. High School is enduring. . . . No one is completely delivered from the days of High School" (*Sports Illustrated*, August 31, 1981, p. 38).

Thank God his conclusion is not true. We can be delivered from the scars and damages and lies of our early years. Thank God His redeeming grace can break the chains of our sinful past, and His reprogramming grace can dissolve the compulsions of our wrongly computerized past.

I heard a beautiful testimony from one of the converts in a Bill Glass Prison Crusade in the South. He was a huge man with his arm in a sling. They told us he was known as one of the tough guys of the prison. He accepted Christ as his Savior on the first night of the crusade. A few days later he said, "You know, something's happening to me. I don't really understand it and I sure can't explain it. I got up this morning and I didn't scream and holler like I usually do. Even my cellmates commented about it. The only way I can describe it is it's like someone took the old tape which had been playing in my mind since I was a kid and put a new tape in and it's playing new talk and new music."

This was an amazing insight for a comparatively uneducated person. He was already beginning to experience the renewing and reprogramming process. Sometime later he discovered another important factor and added, "But you know, I've got to keep working on it and see to it that the right tapes are playing."

He had discovered his responsibility. Just in case anyone has gotten the wrong idea from anything we've said—the reason we try to discover damages from the past is not to blame someone else. Rather, it is to clarify our insights and outline the real issues, so that we can direct our prayer and efforts to the right places.

It is amazing to what lengths some people will go to avoid their own responsibility. In March 1978, a Colorado man brought a "malparenting suit" against his mother and father. He sued them for $300,000 for "lousing up his life," claiming they had intentionally done a terrible job of parenting and had made him what he was. The judge dismissed the suit saying there must be a "statute of limitations" on parenting and a time when an adult takes responsibility for his own life. If not, then next will come suits against brothers, sisters, teachers, and even friends.

Jesus had an amazing way of cutting through all excuses and attempts to scapegoat others. He always made people face up to their responsibility. If we were all honest we would agree that the problem is really in ourselves. Just as the fingers and the thumb are rooted in the palm of the hand, so our problems are rooted in the self. And this self needs three spiritual experiences to come into wholeness: forgiveness, healing, and surrender.

PERSONAL
REFLECTION

■ Have you gotten stuck in the "blame game"—choosing to play the role of victim rather than acknowledging the past and moving on to take responsibility for the present? Who are you blaming and for what? What are you doing to take responsibility for your own life in the present?

_____

_____

_____

_____

_____

When an airplane crashes, a lot of attention is focused on the "little black box." This is the crashproof, fireproof, waterproof steel box which contains the recording of everything the pilots said and did just prior to the accident. When the investigators get that then they are able to make an accurate determination of who or what was at fault.

In a sense God has built into every one of us a device similar to the flight recorder. Our memories contain the unerring and unerasable record of our every word and action. Conscience is a part of this—so many of us constantly struggle with a sense of unresolved guilt. Sometimes it is a mixture of real guilt and childish pseudoguilt. In any case we are like the psalmist who said, "My sin is ever before me." Note, he did not say "was." He put it in the present tense. We say the trouble is our past, but the real trouble is that the past is not in the past. It is in the present and we wear it around our necks like a chain.

If it is true that forgiveness is the most therapeutic fact in all of life, then guilt must be the most destructive. We are simply not built for it, so we automatically try to atone for it, to get rid of it somehow. Often we carry it around in our bodies and minds, and it affects our entire personality. Or we put it into a bag and dump it on to someone else.

There is only one place we can put our guilt to find a true sense of forgiveness—on the back of the crucified Christ. Isaiah 53:6 says, "All of us like sheep have gone astray. Each of us has turned to his own way. But the Lord has caused the iniquity of us all to fall on Him." And 1 Peter 2:24 declares that "He Himself bore our sins in His body on the cross." We do not have to bear guilt and condemnation any longer. But there will be no moving away from childish burdens of guilt and moving into mature freedom and peace until we can *katargeo* our guilty and unforgiven selves.

## PERSONAL REFLECTION

■ Make a list of things which cause you to *feel* guilty. Go as far back into your memory as you can to retrieve those "guilt-laden" experiences.

_____

_____

_____

_____

_____

■ Why do you think you continue to feel guilty about certain things? How have you learned to deal with guilt in your life?

_____

_____

_____

_____

I have written much about the healing of the memories. Not long ago I was suddenly struck with the thought that God too has had a healing of His memories. In one sense, the Cross involves the mystery of God's memory. There are several places in Scripture which imply that God no longer remembers our sins against us: "Do not remember the sins of my youth or my transgressions" (Psalm 25:7), and "Do not remember the iniquities of our forefathers against us" (79:8).

In commenting on this remarkable fact, Corrie ten Boom puts it in her own inimitable way, "When God forgives He forgets. He buries our sins in the sea and puts a sign on the bank saying, 'No Fishing Allowed.'" The most helpful word I ever heard on this was from a young man who said every time he started to pray, he would remind God of a certain failure in his past. One day when he started to do this it was as though God whispered to him, "My son, enough of that. Stop reminding Me of that sin. I distinctly remember forgetting it a long time ago!"

The first step toward Christian adulthood is to be done with any subtle form of inner penance and self-condemnation for already forgiven and forgotten sins. The guilty self needs to become the forgiven self.

PERSONAL
REFLECTION

■ Psalm 86:5 (TLB) reminds us of this reality: "O Lord, You are so good and kind, so ready to forgive, so full of mercy for all who ask Your aid." What subtle forms of inner penance and self-condemnation have kept you from experiencing God's free and full forgiveness?

_____

_____

_____

_____

■ Apply Psalm 86:5 to any guilt-ridden areas of your life by completing the following sentence.

O Lord, I know You are good and kind and that You are so ready to forgive me for . . . (name any and all sins for which you need to feel forgiven)

_____

_____

_____

_____

_____

_____

There is a figure of speech we often use to express the idea of a wrong response to something: "That's like waving a red flag in a bull's face." Whenever a bull sees the color red he gets furiously angry. This is why the Spanish matadors use red cloaks in their bullfights. Whenever the bull sees the red, he automatically lowers his head, paws the ground with his feet, and charges.

Our personalities are something like that, and one way to look at our childish responses is to consider them as various colored flags of life. Jesus must have realized this basic principle when He warned His disciples, "Keep watching and praying, that you may not enter into temptation; the spirit is willing, but the flesh is weak" (Matthew 26:41). He recognized that every person has his own set of predispositions. Note that word: *Pre*—prior, beforehand—and *disposition*. Predispositions are those things within a person which are prior to his disposition, and which push it in a certain direction. These are the person's own private set of flags which, when waved before him, trigger certain responses. These unchristianized complexes and unhealthy pushes from the past keep dragging him back and pulling him down. In spite of repenting and reading, pleading and praying, his childish responses keep playing the same old record.

One Sunday when we were serving Communion, the crowd was unusually large and it seemed to be taking far more time than normal. The longer it took, the more upset I got. I became overanxious and began to perspire. All of a sudden I saw myself as I really was and said, "This is utterly ridiculous. Here I am, standing here in my holy robe at the altar of the church, getting flustered because we are going to be a few minutes late." And then I saw something else. I saw myself as a young boy with my schedule-maniac grandmother. She was the kind who had to be at the train station forty-five minutes ahead of schedule just to be on time. I could almost hear her prodding me, "Hurry up, David. What's taking you so long? Hurry up, or we'll be late." Then I prayed silently, "Lord, set me free from this. I do this every time something makes the service run over a few minutes, and I'm tired of letting that flustered little boy run my life." I was able to relax and can honestly say that it has not troubled me since. Up to that point, a tight schedule was like waving a red flag in my face—it produced in me a response of hurried overanxiety. But what about you?

## PERSONAL REFLECTION

■ What kinds of situations trigger particularly strong emotional responses in you? Describe a few.

_____

_____

_____

_____

_____

_____

■ *Red flags of resentment.* When your husband or wife, child or friend says or does a certain thing, is there an immediate negative response of resentment? If so, deep down within you a red flag has been waved. The place you experience this most strongly is in the closeness of marriage and the home. Someone has described these predispositions as the "furniture of marriage"—the basic personality equipment and responses people bring into marriage. It can be as simple as a wife saying, "Honey, would you please take out the garbage?" The red flag has been waved and the bull, I mean, the husband—roars and charges. Or the husband cautions his wife about the grocery bill and she bristles, remembering her penny-pinching childhood.

## PERSONAL REFLECTION

■ What types of situations elicit a sense of resentment in you? Name some.

_____

_____

_____

_____

_____

■ *Yellow flags of fear.* We sometimes say of a person, "He's yellow," meaning he is afraid or cowardly. Fear can cause some powerful and paralyzing reactions. The Bible points out three of man's greatest fears.

First is the fear represented by Adam after his sin, recorded in Genesis 3:8-10. When God asked Adam where he was, he answered from his hiding place behind a tree, "I was afraid and I went and hid myself." Adam was afraid that when God found out what he had done and who he really was, he would not be accepted. In Adam's case he had experienced the purest kind of unconditional love. His fear came from guilt and self-accusation.

Today we often see this fear in people who have experienced a highly conditional love. Whatever the source, guilt or inadequate love, this is a very deep-seated fear—"If I am known, known for who I really am, I will not be loved or accepted." The answer to this fear is found in God's great promise, "For God hath not given us a spirit of fear, but . . . love" (2 Timothy 1:7, KJV).

God's unconditional love and grace, which always accepts us where we are today, is the answer to this fear of rejection. Kathy was struggling with both resentment and fear when she came for help. She found it hard to understand acceptance and affirmation. There was always the fear she would be rejected, especially by men. She remembered many times when her father had turned her away: he never had time for her, never listened to her. Once she had seen a wall plaque in a store with some loving sentiments on it. She saved up her money and gave it to her dad. He looked at it and said rather gruffly, "We've got enough junk lying around the house now." She said she remembered something being turned off inside her that day. Later, when her father mellowed and wanted to be more understanding and affectionate she was still angry and afraid. It had affected her relationships with people and with God. Gradually she learned to forgive and to accept affirmation and love. Through our counseling and the friendship of a loving Christian family, she came to understand the "Daddyness" of God. As she shared and let herself be known, she realized she was accepted and loved.

Another fear is the one expressed by the one-talented man in Jesus' parable (Matthew 25:14-30). His was the common fear of not being useful in life. He buried his one talent because he was afraid the Master would be harsh and overdemanding. This kind of fear troubles many who were brought up on the "measure-up" philosophy of life. They see God and people as asking them to do too much and to be too much—more than they are capable of. "But God has not given us a spirit of fear, but of . . . power." God never asks of us what He will not supply. "The One who calls you is faithful and He will do it" (1 Thessalonians 5:23, NIV). As we have heard so often, "It is not our ability but our availability."

There is a fear which Job expressed: "For what I fear comes upon me and what I dread befalls me. I am not at ease, nor am I quiet, and I am not at rest, but turmoil comes" (Job 3:25-26). This is the fear that I will not be adequate, I will not be able to cope with life. So many people talk to me about the fear that they will have a nervous breakdown as their mother or father did. Or they are afraid to marry because their marriage may end up in divorce. So many people today fear that they will reproduce the tragedies and traumas of their childhood homes. Again the Word of God comes to the rescue: "For God has not given us a spirit of timidity but of power and love and discipline." God is in the business of breaking vicious cycles. He is the God who specializes in the new start. Not just the second chance, but the first chance—the chance to start a whole new positive cycle of love and goodness. He is in the business of tearing down ancient yellow flags of fear.

## PERSONAL REFLECTION

■ Of the three "flags of fear" Dr. Seamands mentions above—(1) the fear of rejection, (2) the fear of insignificance, (3) the fear of inadequacy—which one(s) paralyze your life the most? Please explain.

_____

_____

_____

_____

_____

_____

■ *Black flags of abuse.* So many people have the black, or at least gray, incidents of life which leave them feeling soiled, dirty, and ashamed. These may have happened during the sensitive childhood years, the stormy years of pubescence and adolescence, or the impressionable years of young adulthood. They involve the area of sexual experiences. It is difficult to say whether this kind of tragic and traumatic experience is on the increase, or if it is just being talked about more openly. My personal opinion is that the incidence of sexual abuse is definitely increasing, because of the sexual wilderness in which we live where there are so few moral fences.

My files are filled with letters from people who have come for help and liberation from sexual experiences which have left deep scars so that they have not been able to respond naturally and normally during courtship and then in the intimacies of marriage. But these are also some of the most joyous and exciting letters of deliverance, cleansing, and healing. A woman freed from the binding chains of a lesbian relationship wrote:

> At this point I am just waiting on God and His direction. I feel as though a malignant tumor has been removed from the center of my being and I am very restful and quiet. At the same time I feel a sense of excitement and anticipation. It is as though Jesus is reaching down inside of me and gently pulling out pieces of myself to show me what is there. . . . Some things I know have been turned over to Him. Others have been healed, and where I used to feel sick, I now feel whole. He is teaching me who I can be in Him.

Many subsequent years of happy married life confirm the depth of her healing.

My favorite letter is from Irene. I had spent many hours with her when she was a student in college, which led to a long session of prayer for the healing of those scalding and sordid memories of sexual abuse by her own father. I didn't hear from her for many years and then came a long letter. Her father had been taken seriously ill and had asked to see her before he died. She made the trip in fear and trepidation.

> I wasn't sure how I would feel about Daddy—whether my emotions had really been healed as I trusted they were, or whether when coming into close physical proximity I would still feel that wave of nausea and all the words of love and concern, even though they came from my heart, would have to be forced through my lips. . . .
>
> The two weeks I was there with Mom and Dad were fantastic. I could almost feel the Lord hugging me close to Him, with His arms around me, guiding everything I said and did! It was a beautiful, unforgettable experience that I praise the Lord for. I wouldn't have missed it for anything! I was filled with His special joy and peace. Outside of Christ I would have been a nervous wreck and no help to anyone.
>
> When I saw Daddy, there seemed to be an instant rapport and understanding between us, and with honest and joyful love I threw my arms around his frail, thin body, kissed him and told him I loved him. He had tears streaming down his face. He knew and I knew that everything in the past was forgiven and washed in the blood of the Lamb. There was healing and wholeness and unspoken understanding. My heart soared! The healing and love for which I had trusted the Lord so long ago was mine, not just when I was far enough away from the problem to be able to accept it in theory, but right there in Daddy's arms. I wanted to call you right away to share it all with you, but I wouldn't have been able to explain the call to Mama, so I just promised to write you.

She then went on to describe the privilege of helping lead her father to a personal experience of Christ in his final weeks of life and their fellowship together.

PERSONAL
REFLECTION

■ What "black" or at least "gray" incidents of childhood have left you feeling soiled, dirty, and ashamed? Name them specifically. How about incidents from your teenage or young adult years? How about incidents in the present?

**Childhood Incidents**_____

_____

_____

_____

_____

**Teenage/Young Adult Incidents** _____

_____

_____

_____

_____

**Present-Day Incidents of Abuse** _____

_____

_____

_____

_____

■ *White flag of surrender.* Paul reminds us that God has given us weapons of warfare which are strong enough for "the destruction of fortresses." For we are "destroying speculation and every lofty thing raised up against the knowledge of God, and we are taking every thought captive to the obedience of Christ" (2 Corinthians 10:4-5). The final sign of the capture of the fortress is when the enemy flag is torn down.

One of the most exciting and interesting experiences of our missionary career was to witness the transfer of power from Britain to India. We gathered with thousands on August 15, 1947 to watch as the British flag (the Union Jack) was slowly lowered and the tricolor flag of the newly independent India was hoisted in its place. The local police band added a touch of humor by playing "London Bridge Is Falling Down!" In spite of the musical selection, it was an awesome and exciting hour.

But I have had an even greater privilege—that of being with hundreds of people when, through the wisdom and the power of God, ancient strongholds of childishness, infirmity, and immaturity were pulled down and the Christian flag raised up.

But before this could happen there was always a series of struggles. These took many forms which involved all parts of the total personality—mind, emotion, and will. There were all kinds of major and minor skirmishes, in which childish things were done away with. Ultimately there came the decisive battle when the full surrender was made, when the defeated and ofttimes battered self ran up the white flag of unconditional surrender. Then the Christian flag was hoisted and Christ could claim full lordship over His own.

Have you ever noticed what the Christian flag really is? It is simply a clean white flag with the cross imprinted on a small section of blue. It is the emblem of the conquering Christ implanted on the sign of our surrender.

A man was once asked, "Sir, are you a Christian?" He was thoughtful for a few moments and then replied, "Yes—in spots." My prayer is that you will allow the Holy Spirit to make you a spotless and mature child of God.

## PRAYERFUL REFLECTION

■ The ultimate spiritual battle we wage is that of surrendering ourselves unconditionally to the lordship of Christ. With God's help, what childish things do you hope to put away so that you can be a growing and mature child of God? As a closing prayer, draw your own "white flag of surrender." Use words and symbols to express the victories you expect to have as the result of letting Christ claim full lordship in your life.

**My White Flag of Unconditional Surrender**

## PERSONAL RENEWAL

■ One of the greatest challenges of "putting away childish things" is to DO what you KNOW. As you tackle this challenge head-on in the weeks to come, let the words of the Apostle Paul in Philippians 4:9 give you courage to keep pressing on toward emotional and spiritual maturity.

> *The things you have learned and received and heard and seen in me, practice these things; and the God of peace shall be with you.*

# PART TWO

# APPENDIX ONE

## GROUP STUDY FORMAT

This workbook is designed for use both by individuals or in various group settings—such as support groups, Bible studies, or Sunday School classes.

Allow a minimum of 13 weeks for group study, focusing on one chapter of the book a week. Limit the length of each meeting to two hours.

### How to Get a Group Started

Probably the best place to begin is by contacting the pastor of your church and letting him know of your interest in starting a support group using *Putting Away Childish Things* as the basis of your study. Tell him why you feel a study of this nature would be valuable to the members of the church and also how it can serve as an outreach to the community. Once you have acquired the necessary approval, find a meeting location and establish a date and time to begin the group.

A word about your meeting place. It should be a neutral setting rather than someone's home, if possible. Homes are often full of distractions (e.g., children, telephone calls). It is difficult to maintain an environment of strict confidentiality when family members are home. A room in the church can actually provide one of the safest places for your group to meet.

The next step is to get the word out about your group. You should be able to fill a group quickly by running an ad in your church bulletin and in the church activities section of your local newspaper. Ideally, your group should have six to twelve members, but start with fewer if necessary. In time, a support group that is working right will promote itself and you will not lack for group participants.

### Meeting Format for Week 1 ONLY

1. Start on time. Welcome people as they arrive and make sure each person has a copy of the *Putting Away Childish Things Workbook*. Provide beverages if you wish. Ask everyone to complete and wear a name tag during your first meeting.

SPECIAL NOTE: Group participants should be asked to purchase their own copy of the *Putting Away Childish Things Workbook* from a local Christian bookstore. Or, for the convenience of those who attend, you (the sponsoring church/organization) may choose to purchase a quantity of the books ahead of time and let group members buy them back from you at your first meeting.

2. Introduce yourself as the person who ran the ad. Explain that you would like the group to be a source of support for yourself and everyone present. Also let everyone know that the group is designed as a 13-week program, including this first meeting.

3. Explain that leadership will rotate within the group so that each week a different member will lead the group. It is the responsibility of the person leading to start the meeting on time, remind group members of the writing assignment for the following week, and to find another leader for the following week, prior to closing the meeting.

4. Emphasize that everything that is said during the meeting is to remain in the meeting, that none of what is shared should be discussed outside the group. This is *crucial* to the effectiveness of the program.

5. Explain that it would be helpful for everyone to hear one another's reasons for coming to the group and invite each person to take up to five minutes to talk about what made him or her decide to attend. Let group participants know that no one has to talk for that long, but that this amount of time is available for anyone who wants it. Volunteer to begin by giving your name and briefly telling your own story.

6. Ask group members to turn to the Personal Journey Summary Sheet for Week 1 on page 225. Explain that the basic format for each meeting will be that of a writing workshop. Group members will be asked to write down their response to each of the questions listed on the page for that week. They will normally be given 15 minutes to do their writing. A three-minute warning prior to the end of the writing time will be given to let group members know they should be writing their answer for the final question on the page.

7. Ask group members to take 10 minutes at this point to complete their writing for the Personal Journey Summary Sheet, Week 1. Give a three-minute warning prior to the end of the writing time.

8. Go around the group and have each person read what he or she has written for *only* the last question on the sheet. Anyone may "pass" if they do *not* wish to answer the question, but encourage as many as possible to participate.

9. Discuss the Guidelines for Group Sharing which are spelled out on page 224.

10. Ask if anyone has a prayer request regarding themselves or others. Note those requests, then close in prayer for the group.

11. Ask if someone would be willing to lead the group the following week.

12. Remind group members to read and work the journaling exercises in Chapter 1 for the following week.

**Meeting Format for Weeks 2–13**

1. Welcome everyone. Have first-time visitors introduce themselves by name.

2. Ask group members to join you for a moment of silent prayer. Encourage everyone to focus their thoughts and open their hearts and minds to what the Holy Spirit wants to say to them during this week's discussion.

3. Have group members turn to the Personal Journey Summary Sheet for the week and spend 15 minutes writing down their response to each of the questions listed on the page. Give a three-minute warning prior to the end of the writing time.

4. If there are more than ten of you present at your meeting, split into smaller groups of five or six each for Family Group Sharing (described in the next step).

5. Family Group Sharing: Designate one person in each group as the lead reader. This means that that person begins the time of sharing by reading his or her answer to the first question on the page. Then proceeding around the circle, everyone in the group may take a turn reading what he or she has written for that question. IMPORTANT NOTE: Anyone in a family group may "pass" if he or she does *not* wish to read his or her answer to the question. Repeat this same process for each of the questions on the page. Before breaking into family groups, review these simple rules for sharing (see the next step).

6. Rules for Family Group Sharing: ■ Allow equal time for each family member to share; ■ Please limit individual sharing to explanations of the written material; ■ Feedback from family members may be offered only after every person in the family group has had an opportunity to share what he or she has written for the question being answered.

7. Reassemble the whole group after approximately 60 minutes. Ask if anyone would like to share anything from their reading and writing experience during the week, or something they learned during this week's Family Group Sharing time.

8. Spend the last 15 minutes of your meeting in prayer. Ask if anyone wants to share a prayer request regarding themselves or others. Then pray for one another.

9. Let group members know what the reading and writing assignment is for the following week. Encourage everyone to complete that work prior to coming to the next week's meeting.

10. Ask if someone would be willing to lead the group the following week.

# GUIDELINES FOR GROUP SHARING

Each person experiences emotional healing at a different pace. But everyone's healing process is enhanced by the mutual support and encouragement that is found in a group setting. The following guidelines will help keep the group process healthy. Take time to read these guidelines aloud at each session, if necessary, as a reminder of the way the group process should work.

**Group Guidelines**

1. Remember that trust grows over time. Share only as much as what feels safe for you. Risk sharing more when you feel safe doing so.

2. Be an attentive listener. You can learn much from other people's insights if you will take time to really hear what they are saying.

3. Maintain confidences. Remember that anything that is said in the group is considered confidential and must not be shared outside the group unless specific permission is given to do so. Memorize this rule: WHO YOU SEE HERE, WHAT IS SAID HERE, WHEN YOU LEAVE HERE, LET IT STAY HERE. This is crucial to the effectiveness of this program.

4. Limit your sharing to what is written on your summary sheet. This will allow everyone in the group who wishes to share, the opportunity to do so.

5. Talk only about yourself and your own situation. Avoid getting into conversations that focus on other people (including your spouse, children, friends, etc.).

6. Avoid giving advice. Everyone is welcome to share their personal experience and what has worked for them in the healing process, but no one is to advise another person about what he or she should do.

7. No cross-talk. Cross-talk is when two people engage in a conversation that excludes the other members of the group. Speak only when it is your turn.

8. Be as honest with yourself and others as you possibly can be. Pray for the other members of the group. Remember what James tells us: "Confess your sins to one another and pray for each other so God can heal you" (James 5:16, NCV).

## PERSONAL JOURNEY SUMMARY SHEET
### *"Telling My Story"*

*MEETING FOCUS: The best way to begin is to share your story, because doing so will forge an immediate bond and foster a sense of belonging.*

■ What made you decide to come to this group? Briefly describe what has been happening in your life that makes the topic of "putting away childish things" relevant to your life.

_____

_____

_____

_____

_____

_____

_____

■ What TV show best describes your family during your childhood years? "Leave It to Beaver"? "The Waltons"? "The Brady Bunch"? "Father Knows Best"? "All in the Family"? "Dallas"? "The Simpsons"? Why?

_____

_____

_____

_____

_____

_____

■ We all have childish behaviors that keep us from growing up emotionally and spiritually. What childish behaviors or attitudes have you noticed in your own life?

_____

_____

_____

_____

_____

■ What would you like to see God do in your life as the result of going through this workbook, *Putting Away Childish Things*?

_____

_____

_____

_____

_____

_____

# PERSONAL JOURNEY SUMMARY SHEET
## *Chapter 1—The Hidden Child in Us All*

*MEETING FOCUS: The hidden child of your past is very much alive and affects everything that you do—for good or for bad.*

■ Describe yourself as a child. Recall in as much detail as you can the child you remember being. Focus on *who you were,* more than on *what you did* as a child.

_____

_____

_____

_____

_____

■ As an adult, have you ever behaved in ways that others viewed as childish and inappropriate? Describe those behaviors and tell what responses those behaviors elicited from other adults.

_____

_____

_____

_____

_____

■ The hardest place to live maturely is with the people who are closest to you. How do you respond when someone you love confronts you about what they perceive to be an immature behavior of yours? Give an example of a time this happened.

_____

_____

_____

_____

_____

_____

_____

■ The Holy Spirit will work in your life to show you where you need to "grow up" if you are willing to surrender your pride and face yourself honestly. Are you ready to face this challenge? Describe what motivates you to begin this process in your life or what keeps you at present from beginning the journey.

_____

_____

_____

_____

_____

# PERSONAL JOURNEY SUMMARY SHEET
## *Chapter 2—The Healing of the Memories*

*MEETING FOCUS: God may lead you back through a painful memory of the past in order to restore your relationships with Him and others.*

■ Our minds have a phenomenal capacity to record data. Describe a time when a memory you had pushed from your conscious mind came back to you by way of a dream or through something you heard, saw, or experienced in the present.

_____

_____

_____

_____

_____

■ Painful memories are not automatically evicted or transformed by an experience of conversion, the filling of the Holy Spirit, or even through growth in grace. Are you aware of any ways in which your spiritual growth has been stunted because of unresolved painful memories from the past? What part of your relationship with God seems to cause you the most grief?

_____

_____

_____

_____

_____

■ In chapter 2, Dr. Seamands describes a type of prayer that involves the healing of memories. Express how you feel about the use of prayer in the healing of memories. Have you ever experienced this type of healing in your life? Describe your experience. If not, would you like to? Why?

_____

_____

_____

_____

_____

_____

■ While healing prayer does apply to *some,* it does not necessarily apply to *everybody.* Emotional healing, for most people, is a long and painful process. Write a prayer expressing to God what you need from Him at this point in your healing process.

_____

_____

_____

_____

_____

_____

## PERSONAL JOURNEY SUMMARY SHEET
### *Chapter 3—A Childhood Motto Which Destroys Adults*

*MEETING FOCUS: Here's some good news—you do not have to "measure up" in order to be loved or approved of by God.*

■ Describe what your spiritual walk with God has looked like over the past six months. What would you say has most influenced your spiritual life during this time?

_____

_____

_____

_____

_____

■ What type of God do you have? Describe Him as you know Him today. (How do you *experience* God in your heart—not just *know* Him in your head?)

_____

_____

_____

_____

_____

■ Dr. Seamands states, " . . . this motto, 'Measure up,' camouflages and sabotages true Christian holiness more than any other." In what ways have you tried to win God's approval and love by "doing right"? Do you ever feel resentful toward God and/or other people because all your efforts of trying to "measure up" never seem to be quite enough? Why do you think you try so hard and feel so resentful?

_____

_____

_____

_____

_____

_____

■ You can neither do anything SO BAD, nor anything SO GOOD to deserve more or less of God's love and grace. He gives both freely—unconditionally. Express how you feel about no longer having to "measure up" in order to be loved or approved of by God.

_____

_____

_____

_____

_____

_____

# PERSONAL JOURNEY SUMMARY SHEET
## *Chapter 4—Another Childhood Motto*

*MEETING FOCUS: As a Christian, you are free to feel and express your emotions—both good and bad.*

■ What message(s) did your parents communicate to you as a child about having and expressing feelings?

_____

_____

_____

_____

■ In chapter 4, Dr. Seamands discusses three emotions that are often difficult for people to express—grief and sorrow, anger, and deep agony. How do you handle these emotions in your life?

_____

_____

_____

_____

■ Name two or three of the most significant losses you've experienced in your life. What steps have you taken to grieve those losses? What more might you need to do to complete the grief process in your life in relation to those losses?

_____

_____

_____

_____

■ Make a list of four situations in your life that have caused you to feel angry. How was your anger expressed in each situation?

_____

_____

_____

_____

_____

■ What situations have caused you to "agonize" over knowing and doing God's will in your life?

_____

_____

_____

_____

_____

■ Dr. Seamands states, "Mature holiness means recovering our true humanness." The truth is, you will be only as spiritually mature as you are emotionally whole. How committed are you to your own process of emotional and spiritual recovery? In the form of a prayer of commitment, let God know how you feel about the things you discovered about yourself as you worked through the material in chapter 4 this week.

_____

_____

_____

_____

_____

# PERSONAL JOURNEY SUMMARY SHEET
## *Chapter 5—Childish Ideas of Love and Marriage*

*MEETING FOCUS: Growing into real maturity means getting rid of your childish understanding about love and marriage.*

■ What are some "fairy tale" fantasies of love and marriage you've held onto?

_____

_____

_____

_____

_____

■ Describe what you think enduring love looks like. Have you experienced this kind of love in your life? If not, why not?

_____

_____

_____

_____

_____

■ One of the greatest problems in marriage is communication. The Apostle Paul defined what he meant by mature communication when he wrote, "So that we may no longer be children, tossed to and fro . . . rather, speaking the truth in love, we are to grow up in every way" (Ephesians 4:14-15, RSV). Give an example of a time when someone spoke the truth to you in an *unloving* way. Then describe an instance when a person's kind and loving words got a hard-hitting truth through to your desensitized heart.

_____

_____

_____

_____

_____

_____

■ In learning to "speak the truth in love" we recognize that this may
mean confrontation and conflict. How did your parents resolve
their conflicts? How do you view and handle conflict today as an
adult?

_____

_____

_____

_____

_____

■ What would you like to see happen in the days and months ahead
as you let God *katargeo* your fairy-tale thinking into a growing,
maturing concept of love and marriage?

_____

_____

_____

_____

_____

# PERSONAL JOURNEY SUMMARY SHEET
## *Chapter 6—Childish Ideas of God and His Will*

*MEETING FOCUS: To grow up emotionally and spiritually, you must get rid of your inadequate, immature concepts of God and how He works His will in this world.*

■ Have you at any time found it difficult to accept and understand an incident in your life as being "God's will"? Describe one or two confusing situations you've faced in relationship to God's will.

_____

_____

_____

_____

■ What do you find to be the most challenging part of knowing and doing the will of God in your life?

_____

_____

_____

_____

■ Respond to this statement: "Nothing can happen to you that God cannot use for good." In what ways does your life bear out the truth of this statement? Describe at least one painful circumstance from your life that God redeemed and used for your ultimate good.

_____

_____

_____

_____

■ Take a moment to think about the various episodes in your life that have involved mishaps, wrong decisions, and apparent coincidences. Let the following prayer from *Someone Who Beckons* by Timothy Dudley-Smith (IVP) lead you as you spend time in quiet reflection.

> *Lord of my life,*
> *How many things have happened to me that might have happened otherwise! Looking back, upon what slender threads Your pattern for me hung! What insignificant weights tilted the scale from this to that! And from this multitude of tiny choices, unrelated circumstances, unnoticed influences, You wove the pattern of my present life!...And all this that I recall, only the tip of the iceberg! What of the unseen providences? What of the choices before I was born or thought of? I join, Lord, with the children in their song of praise: "Thank You, Father, for making me me."*
>
> *And if this is true of my past life, shaped, subtly and beyond imagining, by the finger of God—why, I rest my future on Your promise too. You know Your plans, Lord, as You did for Israel in exile. Knowing that the plans are Yours, I do not need to know much else about them. Except this: that all You do is good. So let me seek You, Lord, Your face, Your Word, Your presence and Your will, with all my heart. Amen.*

Write several sentence prayers expressing to God how you've come to know at a heartfelt level that His will for you is "good, acceptable and perfect."

_____

_____

_____

_____

_____

_____

# PERSONAL JOURNEY SUMMARY SHEET
## *Chapter 7—Childish Ideas of Prayer*

*MEETING FOCUS: You may doubt the effectiveness and worthwhileness of prayer if you are holding onto some childish ideas of prayer.*

■ Complete the following statements:

*My greatest disillusionment about prayer came when* _____

_____

_____

*My greatest reassurance about prayer came when* _____

_____

_____

■ Half-truths about prayer, even those spoken by the most well-intentioned people, can be particularly devastating. What half-truths about prayer have left you feeling confused or resentful toward God or other people?

_____

_____

_____

_____

_____

_____

■ Dr. Seamands reminds us that "Sometimes God does not answer the *want* we express in order that He might answer what He knows to be the real *need* behind it." Has this been your experience? Describe a time when God gave you what you needed rather than what you thought you wanted. Have you ever felt disappointed with God's *provision* in your life? Explain.

_____

_____

_____

_____

_____

_____

■ Have you ever asked God to bail you out of a situation, and His answer was to let you work through it on your own? What happened? How do you balance personal responsibility (doing what you can) with childlike dependability on God (letting Him do what only He can do)? Give a personal example of a time you did this.

_____

_____

_____

_____

_____

_____

■ Write a letter of thanks to God expressing to Him why you are grateful He doesn't always answer your prayers according to what you ask.

_____

_____

_____

_____

_____

# PERSONAL JOURNEY SUMMARY SHEET
## *Chapter 8—Childhood Confusions Versus Adult Distinctions*

*MEETING FOCUS: If you are going to function as a healthy, growing Christian you must be able to distinguish between approval and acceptance, temptation and sin, and hurt and harm.*

■ Dr. Seamands writes, "Some of us have never learned that it is possible to hold the highest moral standards and at the same time be accepting and loving toward those who have violated those standards." Demonstrate your understanding of this distinction by giving an example of your doing this in the life of another person.

_____

_____

_____

_____

■ Even as adults we need to know we are loved and accepted in spite of the things we do wrong. What do you think is the difference between unconditional *love* and unconditional *acceptance*? How do you let the people you care about know that your acceptance of them does not depend on your approval of everything they do?

_____

_____

_____

_____

■ Every one of us experiences temptations. Giving into temptation begins with a series of small compromises. Think of a time when you gave into temptation. Describe the series of compromising choices you made along the way which ultimately led to your giving into the temptation.

_____

_____

_____

_____

_____

■ What positive steps have you learned to take to keep yourself from yielding to temptation?

_____

_____

_____

■ Express how you feel about the distinction Dr. Seamands makes between God *hurting* you, but never *harming* you.

_____

_____

_____

■ What are some of the painful experiences God has used to bring about a positive change or new level of emotional or spiritual maturity in your life?

_____

_____

_____

_____

# PERSONAL JOURNEY SUMMARY SHEET
## *Chapter 9—Childish Dependency on Feelings*

*MEETING FOCUS: An unhealthy dependence on feelings will cause confusion when it comes to your faith in God, understanding His will for your life, and learning how to obediently respond to the Spirit's voice.*

■ Think of one or two recent instances when your feelings controlled your behavior. Write down what happened.

_____

_____

_____

_____

_____

_____

■ Dr. Seamands mentions three situations in our lives when we must be careful *not to* have an unhealthy dependence on feelings—(1) when it comes to feeling assured of our salvation; (2) when we are trying to discern God's will for our lives; or (3) when we feel God calling us to serve Him. Why do you think an overdependence on feelings is a MUST NOT in each of these situations?

_____

_____

_____

_____

_____

■ If you grew up in a home where feelings were discounted or rarely expressed, you will find it difficult to trust what you feel. Yet sometimes the Holy Spirit speaks truth to us at the feeling level and if we discount or dismiss feelings we can miss what He is saying to us. Explain how you balance feelings and facts when it comes to your faith.

_____

_____

_____

_____

■ Describe one of the most difficult decisions you've ever had to make. What steps did you take to determine God's will for you in relationship to that decision? What was the outcome? What balance have you achieved between intuition and common sense when seeking God's guidance?

_____

_____

_____

_____

■ Some people depend on feelings as their motivation for doing good works. How do you achieve a balance between "doing good works" because you feel called to serve God in a particular way, and "doing good works" just because the need exists or you feel obligated to do so?

_____

_____

_____

_____

# PERSONAL JOURNEY SUMMARY SHEET
## *Chapter 10—Childish Concepts of Self and Self-Surrender*

*MEETING FOCUS: A childish concept of your "self" will lead to wrong thinking, wrong feeling, and wrong living.*

■ In what ways did the family system you grew up in teach you to get rid of your "self"? How about the religious system you grew up in? How present and alive is your sense of self today?

_____

_____

_____

_____

_____

■ Some Christians have the impression that the less we think of ourselves, the more God will be pleased with us. On the other hand, society overflows with propaganda that would lead us to believe that allowing the self to have full expression is the key to real fulfillment. Where are you in relation to these two extremes?

_____

_____

_____

_____

_____

■ Do you love yourself? Why or why not? Describe behaviors you exhibit that demonstrate healthy self-love?

_____

_____

_____

_____

■ The idea of surrendering, of releasing authority and control of outcomes to another, is a very difficult notion for thinking people. What do you feel when you consider really putting your life and your will—your whole future—in God's hands? What are the specific fears that come to mind when you consider turning all of your life over to the care of God?

_____

_____

_____

_____

■ In closing, write a letter to God. Disclose to Him the area(s) of your life that are the hardest for you to surrender fully to Him. Tell Him honestly why it is difficult for you to trust Him with those parts of your life.

_____

_____

_____

_____

_____

# PERSONAL JOURNEY SUMMARY SHEET
## *Chapter 11—The Ultimate Crisis of Life*

*MEETING FOCUS: Surrendering your "self" to the lordship of Jesus Christ is the ultimate spiritual battle you will wage in life.*

■ Share with the other members of your group the picture you drew this week depicting your own spiritual battlefield of self-surrender.

■ The idea of "giving up control" and "surrendering one's self" are one and the same concept. At the heart of each phrase is the matter of learning to "let go and let God." This is easier said than done. Giving up control and letting God be Lord is a very difficult thing to do. Who is in control of your life right now? To what or whom have you given permission to be the god of your life at this moment?

_____

_____

_____

_____

_____

_____

_____

■ Is there anything in your life that you feel unable to give up your right to at present? What is it? Describe how you feel about giving it up. What is your greatest source of inner conflict concerning the thing(s) you listed in the previous question? What is your greatest fear in surrendering that part of your life—or who you are—to God?

_____

_____

_____

_____

_____

_____

■ Dr. Seamands reminds us that we actually surrender concrete things and situations only as we become consciously aware of them in our lives. Think of a specific situation you are dealing with at present where your emotions and God's will are coming into conflict. Imagine carrying on a conversation with Jesus concerning your struggle. Write out how you think your conversation with Him might go.

_____

_____

_____

_____

_____

■ Read in unison "The Serenity Prayer" found on pages 200-201 to close your time of sharing this week.

# PERSONAL JOURNEY SUMMARY SHEET
## Chapter 12—Reprogramming Grace

*MEETING FOCUS: Forgiveness, healing, and self-surrender are the keys that will open the door to emotional and spiritual wholeness in your life.*

■ "The first step toward Christian adulthood is to be done with any subtle form of inner penance and self-condemnation for already forgiven and forgotten sins. The guilty self needs to become the forgiven self." What are some of the ways you've attempted to deal with guilt other than by the proper means of nailing it to the cross of Jesus? Draw a cross in the space below and then write on that cross specific things for which you still need to feel God's forgiveness.

■ One of the ways we can reprogram grace in our lives is to ask God to heal us of our "predispositions"—those things within us which trigger certain childish responses. Of the three predispositional emotions Dr. Seamands mentions in chapter 12, which one seems to elicit the strongest response from you most often—*resentment, fear,* or *shame* due to abuse? What steps are you willing to take to reprogram your childish responses? Can you think of any

Scripture verses that would help you reprogram your thinking and way of acting? What are they?

_____

_____

_____

_____

■ In the space below, draw a flag that more or less describes what you feel is the current status of your relationship with the Lord. Use words and symbols to express the victories you expect to have as the result of letting God claim full lordship in your life in the days and weeks ahead.

■ One of the greatest challenges of "putting away childish things" is to DO what you KNOW. Philippians 4:9 exhorts us in this way: "The things you have learned and received and heard and seen . . . practice these things." What principles have you learned, what personal truth have you received, what changes have you been eyewitness to as the result of this course? And what do you intend to do with what you now know?

_____

_____

_____

_____

_____

_____

# APPENDIX TWO

## SUPPORT GROUP RESOURCES

### CHRISTIAN RESOURCES

**Alcoholics for Christ, Inc.**
1316 North Campbell Road
Royal Oak, MI 48067
(313) 399-9955

**Alcoholics Victorious**
International Service Office
1700 Eighth Street
Lewiston, ID 83501

**Christian Alcoholics**
Rehabilitation Association
FOA Road
Pocahontas, MS 39072

**Exodus International**
P.O. Box 2121
San Rafael, CA 94912
(415) 454-1017

**Institute for Christian Living**
Riverside Medical Center
Minneapolis, MN 55427
(612) 593-1791

**Liontamers**
2801 North Brea Blvd.
Fullerton, CA 92635-2799

**Minirth-Meier Clinic West**
260 Newport Center Drive #430
Newport Beach, CA 92660
(800) 877-HOPE

**National Association for
Christian Recovery**
P.O. Box 11095
Whittier, CA 90603
(213) 697-6201

**New Life Treatment Centers**
570 Glenneyre, Suite 107
Laguna Beach, CA 92651
(800) 227-LIFE

**Overcomers Outreach, Inc.**
2290 West Whittier Blvd.
La Habra, CA 90631
(213) 697-3994

**Tools for Recovery**
1201 Knoxville Street
San Diego, CA 92110-3718
(800) 873-8384

### SECULAR RESOURCES

**Adult Children of Alcoholics**
Central Service Board
P.O. Box 35623
Los Angeles, CA 90035
(213) 464-4423

**Alcoholics Anonymous**
P.O. Box 459
Grand Central Station
New York, NY 10163
(212) 686-1100

**Al-Anon/Alateen**
Family Group Headquarters, Inc.
P.O. Box 182
Madison Square Station
New York, NY 10159
(800) 344-2666
(212) 302-7240

**Codependents Anonymous**
P.O. Box 33577
Phoenix, AZ 85067-3577
(602) 944-1141

**Debtors Anonymous**
314 West 53rd Street
New York, NY 10018
(212) 969-0710

**Emotions Anonymous**
P.O. Box 4245
St. Paul, MN 55104
(612) 647-9712

**Gamblers Anonymous**
P.O. Box 17173
Los Angeles, CA 90017
(213) 386-8769

**Incest Survivors Anonymous**
P.O. Box 5613
Long Beach, CA 90800

**Narcotics Anonymous**
World Service Office
16155 Wyandotte Street
Van Nuys, CA 91406
(818) 780-3951

**Overeaters Anonymous**
World Service Office
2190 190th Street
Torrance, CA 90504
(213) 320-7941

**Sex Addicts Anonymous**
P.O. Box 3038
Minneapolis, MN 55403
(612) 871-1520

**Sex & Love Addicts Anonymous**
P.O. Box 119
Boston, MA 02258

# SPECIALIZED READING RESOURCES

## BOOKS RELATED TO FAMILY SYSTEMS

- John Bradshaw, *Bradshaw On: The Family* (Deerfield Beach, Florida: Health Communications, Inc.), 1988.
- Rich Buhler, *Love: No Strings Attached* (Nashville: Thomas Nelson Publishers), 1987.
- Dave Carder, Earl Henslin, John Townsend, Henry Cloud, and Alice Brawand, *Secrets of Your Family Tree* (Chicago: Moody Press), 1991.
- David Stoop and James Masteller, *Forgiving Our Parents, Forgiving Ourselves* (Ann Arbor, Michigan: Servant Publications), 1992.
- Jeff Van Vonderen, *Families Where Grace Is in Place* (Minneapolis: Bethany House), 1992.

## BOOKS RELATED TO CODEPENDENCE

- Melody Beattie, *Codependent No More* (New York: Hazelden/Harper), 1987.
- Alfred Ells, *One-Way Relationships Workbook* (Nashville: Thomas Nelson Publishers), 1992.
- Robert Hemfelt, Frank Minirth, and Paul Meier, *Love Is a Choice* (Nashville: Thomas Nelson Publishers), 1989.
- Robert S. McGee, *The Search for Significance* (Houston: Rapha Publishing), 1990.
- J. Keith Miller, *Compelled to Control* (Deerfield, Florida: Health Communications, Inc.), 1992.
- Pia Mellody, *Facing Codependence* (San Francisco: Harper & Row), 1989.

## BOOKS RELATED TO ADULT CHILDREN

- John Bradshaw, *Healing the Shame That Binds You* (Deerfield Beach, Florida: Health Communications, Inc.), 1988.
- Jim Conway, *Adult Children of Legal or Emotional Divorce* (Downers

Grove, Illinois: InterVarsity Press), 1990.
- Richard W. Dickinson, *The Child in Each of Us* (Wheaton, Illinois: Victor Books), 1989.
- Ron Ross, *When I Grow Up . . .* (San Diego: Recovery Publications, Inc.), 1990.
- David Seamands, *Healing for Damaged Emotions* (Wheaton, Illinois: Victor Books), 1981.
- Charles Sell, *Unfinished Business* (Portland, Oregon: Multnomah Press), 1989.

## BOOKS RELATED TO SPIRITUALITY

- Lana L. Bateman, *Bible Promises for the Healing Journey* (Westwood, New Jersey: Barbour Books), 1991.
- Don Crossland, *A Journey Toward Wholeness* (Nashville: StarSong), 1991.
- Friends in Recovery, *The Twelve Steps—A Spiritual Journey* (San Diego: Recovery Publications, Inc.), 1988.
- Earl R. Henslin, *The Way Out of the Wilderness* (Nashville: Thomas Nelson), 1991.
- Mark Johnson, *Spiritual Warfare for the Wounded* (Ann Arbor, Michigan: Servant Publications), 1992.
- C. Christopher Knippers, *Common Sense, Intuition, and God's Guidance* (Nashville: Thomas Nelson), 1993.
- Gordon MacDonald, *Rebuilding Your Broken World* (Nashville: Oliver Nelson), 1988.
- Keith Miller, *A Hunger for Healing* (San Francisco: Harper & Row), 1991.
- David Johnson and Jeff Van Vonderen, *The Subtle Power of Spiritual Abuse* (Minneapolis: Bethany House), 1991.
- Robert A. Schuller, *Dump Your Hang-Ups Without Dumping Them on Others* (Grand Rapids, Michigan: Fleming H. Revell), 1993.
- David A. Seamands, *Healing Grace* (Wheaton, Illinois: Victor Books), 1988.
- Jeff Van Vonderen, *Tired of Trying to Measure Up* (Minneapolis: Bethany House), 1989.

# APPENDIX THREE

## SUPPLEMENTAL JOURNALING PAGES

# PERSONAL JOURNAL

*He gives strength to the weary and increases
the power of the weak. Isaiah 40:29*

# PERSONAL JOURNAL

*Nevertheless I am continually with Thee; Thou hast taken hold of my right hand. PSALM 73:23*

*I know that Thou canst do all things, and that no purpose of Thine can be thwarted.* JOB 42:2

*The Lord is near to all who call upon Him, to all who call upon Him in truth.* PSALM 145:18